Amazing animals
Brilliant science

How DNA technology is being used to help save Scotland's wildlife

Pete Minting

amphibian and reptile
conservation

About the author

Pete Minting works for the Amphibian and Reptile Conservation (ARC) Trust in Scotland. He completed his PhD on the effects of the chytrid fungus *Batrachochytrium dendrobatidis* on natterjack toad populations in the UK in 2012. He has also worked for the University of the Highlands and Islands, Wester Ross Fisheries Trust, Ayrshire Rivers Trust, West Sutherland Fisheries Trust, the Kalahari Meerkat Project, the Rutland Water Osprey Project and the Barbados Sea Turtle Project. He completed a degree in Behavioural Science at the University of Nottingham in 1995, and an MSc in Aquatic Resource Management at King's College, London in 1997.

591

© 2018. Amphibian and Reptile Conservation (ARC) Trust and author Pete Minting

655A Christchurch Road, Boscombe, Bournemouth BH1 4AP United Kingdom

www.arc-trust.org
www.twitter.com/ARC_bytes
www.facebook.com/ARCTrust
www.youtube.com/ARCTrust

A catalogue record for this book is available from the British Library.

ISBN 978-0-9566717-2-1

Book designed by The Design Unit: www.thedesignunit.com

amphibian and reptile
conservation

Foreword

ARC patron and wildlife presenter Chris Packham

I WENT NEWTING EVERY SPRING. IN THE DAYTIME, IT REQUIRED SKILL TO SPOT THE SUPERBLY CAMOUFLAGED SMOOTH AND PALMATE NEWTS RESTING IN THE LEAFY SHALLOWS OF MY LOCAL PONDS AND SCOOP THEM OUT WITH MY HOME-MADE NET.

At night, by torchlight, it was much easier. Their shadows were a giveaway, or I'd spot them wriggling up to snatch a gulp of air from the surface and follow their tails back into the silt below, where with a lucky swipe, I could sieve them out and pop them into a jar. Then I could identify them and see their beautiful orange bellies, the frilly crests of the males and their stripy faces... and best

of all, their tiny, jewel-like eyes. Newts were cool. Indeed, newts are cool!

If you had crouched alongside the young Chris and whispered into his ear that in his lifetime, all you would need to do was take a sample of the water to see if newts lived there, or that this technique could be used to make discoveries about a whole host of fascinating animals, he would have thought you had been watching too much science fiction.

But no, it's true, our advances in the science of DNA, that special molecule which is a personal fingerprint of all life, has been rapid and phenomenal. And now it's becoming more affordable and quicker to do, DNA analysis is becoming an incredibly valuable and important tool in conservation.

This book celebrates and explains how DNA is being used to help lots of different animals. Not just newts but many other amazing species, such as wildcats, badgers, pine martens, water voles, golden eagles and Atlantic salmon. If we use this brilliant science to discover more about these amazing animals, we will be able to start looking after them much better.

Young people have provided some very striking and colourful artworks to help illustrate this book and some tremendous and imaginative essays. I hope you enjoy it, learn from it and want to get more involved in conservation. Science is good, animals are great – together they are the best!
Chris Packham, 2017

Red deer by Jenny O'Gorman, George Watson's College

Contents

Golden eagle

© Laurie Campbell

Introduction

If you read this introduction, you will have a much better understanding of what we are talking about in the rest of this book. Let's start with a surprising biological fact;

Parts of your body have been the same for 530 million years.

How can this possibly be true? You can see that it is true, by looking at the structure of DNA (deoxyribonucleic acid).

What is DNA and what does it do?

DNA is a substance which is found inside the bodies of nearly all living things (organisms) on Earth, including people. The majority of the cells that make up your body contain DNA. You cannot usually see DNA very easily because it is so small but scientists have figured out ways of extracting it, mapping its structure and finding out what it does.

DNA is a chemical with amazing properties. It is DNA that allows complex organisms to reproduce, grow and repair themselves. DNA has been reproducing itself on this planet for a very long time; possibly billions of years. It was only discovered in 1953 but combined with the mysterious forces of electromagnetism that result in chemical reactions, it could be regarded as the 'vital spark' of life which people have been trying to find for centuries. It is likely that it was once a much simpler substance and that somehow it gained the ability to reproduce itself from chemicals found naturally in the environment – either here on planet Earth, or further afield.

How does DNA copy itself?

You may be wondering how DNA manages to copy itself, if it is just a chemical. It is quite a complex chemical, because it is made up of a long chain of simpler chemicals that are joined together. In order to understand how the copying process works, you can think of the chemicals in the long chain as two rows of people, taking part in a ceilidh or a barn dance.

When DNA is not copying itself, the two rows of people are standing opposite each other and holding hands. They are also touching shoulders with the people next to them. Each person is from one of four groups, like the houses in Harry Potter, except that instead of houses such as Gryffindor and Slytherin, there are chemical 'nucleobases' called Adenine, Thymine, Cytosine and Guanine.

DNA HAS BEEN REPRODUCING ITSELF ON THIS PLANET FOR A VERY LONG TIME; POSSIBLY BILLIONS OF YEARS. IT WAS ONLY DISCOVERED IN 1953 BUT COMBINED WITH THE MYSTERIOUS FORCES OF ELECTROMAGNETISM THAT RESULT IN CHEMICAL REACTIONS, IT COULD BE REGARDED AS THE 'VITAL SPARK' OF LIFE WHICH PEOPLE HAVE BEEN TRYING TO FIND FOR CENTURIES.

Simplified diagram of DNA during the copying process

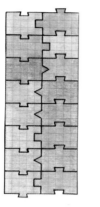 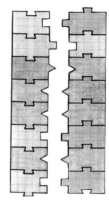

1. Original, double strand of DNA   2. DNA 'unzips' to form two single strands

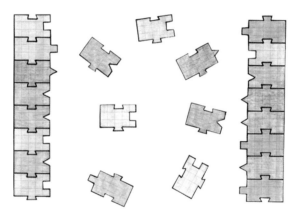

3. New, free nucleobases (made inside the cell) attach to their correct 'partners'

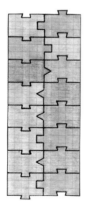 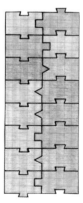

4. When all of the pairs have linked up, this results in two identical copies of the original strand

Key

Adenine   Thymine   Cytosine   Guanine

ALL OF THE INFORMATION NEEDED TO PRODUCE, MAINTAIN AND REPRODUCE LIFE IS RECORDED BY VARIATIONS OF THIS CODING SEQUENCE.

The nucleobases are joined at the shoulders by strong bonds. Their hands are only held together by weak bonds, so they can easily let go. In DNA (and science in general) there is no magic but there are invisible forces that hold chemicals (made up of atoms and molecules) together, or push them apart.

When the 'DNA dance' begins (DNA starts to copy itself), a chemical signal causes the 'hands' of the paired nucleobases to let go. This results in the DNA 'unzipping' from one end towards the other, leaving two long strands held together by strong bonds but with rows of single nucleobases that will attach to any 'free' nucleobases. In the DNA dance, Adenine can only hold hands with Thymine, and Cytosine can only pair with Guanine. If there are plenty of free nucleobases on the 'DNA dance floor' that exists inside a cell, they will attach to the correct nucleobases on the long strands, resulting in two new pieces of DNA with exactly the same sequence as the original piece of DNA.

In a similar 'RNA dance' which is triggered by a different signal, Thymine takes a break and a different nucleobase (Uracil) joins hands with Adenine. This results in the formation of a similar substance called RNA, along each half or strand of the original DNA. This strand of RNA is then released and it helps to make a protein (needed for the growth or repair of organisms), rather than the copying or 'replication' of DNA which is needed for the production of

new cells or bodies. Some tiny, simple organisms such as viruses only contain RNA but are often able to 'hijack' the DNA of other organisms, in order to reproduce themselves.

DNA is the code for life

In DNA, although Adenine (A) always holds hands with Thymine (T), and Cytosine (C) always holds hands with Guanine (G), there is no rule about who can stand shoulder to shoulder. This means that if you read the 'letters' along one side of the DNA chain, it can say almost any sequence involving A, C, G or T (or U, if it is a piece of RNA). All of the information needed to produce, maintain and reproduce life is recorded by variations of this coding sequence. It is quite similar to the coding system used to operate digital technology, except that the code which runs machines like computers and mobile phones consists of ones and zeros, rather than four or five different nucleobases.

You will often hear about 'genes' and DNA in the news. Technically, a gene is a sequence of DNA or RNA that codes for the production of another biochemical (often a protein) with a function. DNA science, or the study of genes, is called genetics. If a gene changes (mutates) or is lost due to a copying error and the wrong protein is made, or not made at all, this can result in a genetic disease. Now it is sometimes possible to modify genes to cure genetic diseases. If the loss or change of a gene turns out to be beneficial, the organism in which it is found will be more likely to survive. This is how evolution works, by the 'natural selection' of individuals that do or do not survive, in a variable and challenging environment, which in the case of planet Earth, has existed for billions of years.

All of these animals have bilateral symmetry; an extinct trilobite, a butterfly and a deer. Scotch Argus butterfly © Butterfly Conservation

There are thousands of genes in the sequence of DNA that makes up the entire 'genome' of an individual human (other living things can have much longer or shorter genomes). Many of the genes in the human genome also occur in other animals. For example, 'homeobox' genes are found in all animals and scientists have identified homeobox sequences that code for the growth of heads, legs and other features (such as symmetrical body plans). If a body plan is the same on two sides, this is called 'bilateral symmetry'. Humans and other mammals are bilaterally symmetrical. So are many other animals, such as butterflies, which are not very closely related but still have some DNA which is the same as ours. The homeobox genes have probably not changed much since 530 million years ago, when the variety of life on Earth rapidly increased. Other genes date back even longer and are common to nearly all living things. If you collected a sample from yourself and used a machine to sequence your own DNA, you could read the sequence of your homeobox genes on the print-out. This is what I meant when I said that parts of your body have been the same for at least 530 million years. Your body will be made of different atoms than the first living animals (because DNA copies and rebuilds itself from simpler chemicals found in the natural environment) but some of the sequences in your own 'DNA instruction manual' for life will be an exact copy, in terms of their physical structure and chemical ingredients. Other parts of your genome will be different, because evolution has resulted in a diverse 'tree of life' with many different organisms but some basic features are common to all of us.

THE HOMEOBOX GENES HAVE PROBABLY NOT CHANGED MUCH SINCE 530 MILLION YEARS AGO, WHEN THE VARIETY OF LIFE ON EARTH RAPIDLY INCREASED. OTHER GENES DATE BACK EVEN LONGER AND ARE COMMON TO NEARLY ALL LIVING THINGS.

Red deer by Jodi MacLellan, Ardnamurchan High School

Cloning or mixing – which is best?

There are two main ways by which new organisms are created, or reproduced, from their parent organisms. Sometimes DNA just copies itself. For example, plants are often exact copies or 'clones' of their parent plants. In biological terms, this can be a relatively 'low-cost' and easy thing to do because it does not require any more complicated structures or processes, than those already described. However, with cloning, the only way that the DNA can change is if there is an error in the copying process, or if the DNA is damaged (a mutation). This does occasionally happen and it can be triggered in a number of ways, for instance by radiation from space (e.g. gamma rays or UV-light). But the rate of change is slow, so a different process is needed if a population of organisms is going to have much variation between individuals, in terms of their DNA codes.

It can be very useful to have some variation in the DNA code because when the environment changes, individuals with different DNA may survive because they are slightly different. Imagine what it was like 66 million years ago, when a huge asteroid crashed into this planet. Temperatures would have changed rapidly, oxygen levels would have declined (as a result of fires) and dust from the impact would have blocked out the sun. The survivors must have had suitable bodies (and DNA) to cope with this. Most dinosaurs did not, so they died out. Environmental change is usually less drastic than that caused by an asteroid impact. But the environment does constantly change, often without us noticing, because our lifetimes are short and the changes are not always obvious.

Although many plants just copy or 'clone' themselves, flowering plants can also mix their DNA with that of other plants. Many modern plants have evolved flowers which allow them to mix their DNA with other closely-related plants and adapt more effectively to their local environment. Many other organisms (including humans) mix their DNA with that of other individuals. This 'sexual' reproduction produces a new generation (in our case, children) that is slightly different to the previous generation. It is like stirring the ingredients of two cake recipes together, resulting in a new cake that has never been made before. This mixing process is a slightly more complicated version of the DNA dance described earlier, which is called 'meiosis'.

During meiosis, genes which are nearly always essential for survival (such as the homeobox genes) are the same in both parents or are kept intact (they are 'conserved'). But other parts of the genome are much more variable, with different versions (called 'alleles') of many genes. When two sexually reproducing organisms mix their genes,

ONE OF THE MOST AMAZING CONCLUSIONS THAT WE CAN DRAW FROM THE STUDY OF DNA IS THAT ALL LIVING THINGS ON EARTH, INCLUDING OURSELVES, PROBABLY HAVE A SINGLE COMMON ANCESTOR.

all of their offspring get a unique mix of these alleles, some from one parent and some from the other. In addition to the potential survival benefits described above, this also means that we can identify unique 'DNA fingerprints' for individuals that have been produced by sexual reproduction.

The only exception is for identical twins (or identical triplets, quadruplets etc), which are created by the splitting of an egg which has already been fertilised, so the mixing of the DNA has already taken place. All of the offspring produced by splitting a fertilised egg have the same sequence of DNA.

Why is inbreeding such a bad idea?

Another feature of sexual reproduction is that faulty DNA is often masked by useful or 'adaptive' DNA which has become dominant over many generations. In nearly all mammals (including humans) each individual gets two versions (alleles) of every gene (one from each parent). As a result of evolution, the dominant allele is

less likely to be faulty (unless it is a 'conserved' gene as described on page 5, in which case, both alleles are the same). If two close relatives (e.g. brother and sister) reproduce, this can result in problems because their DNA is so similar. Because there is less likely to be a 'choice' between alleles, faulty genes which have been masked for generations are more likely to be uncovered and 'expressed' in their offspring. This means that 'inbreeding' (reproducing with close relatives) is often a bad strategy for survival (as we will see later in this book).

DNA is the code for life – but how and where did it begin?

One of the most amazing conclusions that we can draw from the study of DNA is that all living things on Earth, including ourselves, probably have a single common ancestor. At the moment, the oldest fossils found on Earth are thought to be 4.28 billion years old. It is likely that our common ancestor was a smaller and much simpler organism, with far fewer genes but we do not know exactly how it managed to survive. We do not know how a complex, long-chain chemical first formed, or how it later surrounded itself with a protective coat (a cell membrane) and started building the first cells.

We also do not fully understand why the tiny particles (atoms) that make up all substances, including DNA, sometimes join up with each other, or repel each other. If you study physics,

Reality check – 'it's in our DNA' (oh no, it isn't!)
Many business people and politicians have started using the term 'DNA' in ways which are misleading or untrue. For example, if you see an advertisement by a company which claims that 'customer service is in our DNA' this is a lie; the company is just trying to associate itself with something reliable, in order to boost its reputation. Companies are not allowed to modify the DNA of their staff, in order to improve their customer service (well, not yet, anyway!).

DNA from hair can be used to identify animals – in this case, a badger © Laurie Campbell

you will hear about four fundamental forces that are thought to exist, including gravity and electro-magnetism. These forces can result in particle attraction or repulsion in a predictable way, depending upon the substances or atoms involved but we still do not know exactly how or why this happens.

We also do not know whether life began on Earth, or somewhere else in the Universe. Experiments have shown that the nucleobases making up DNA, such as Adenine and Guanine, can be formed from other, simpler chemicals that are commonly found on Earth. But this could theoretically occur elsewhere, so it is possible that the first building blocks of life arrived on a comet or meteorite. When it comes to the origins of life and the Universe, there are plenty of puzzles left to solve.

What is DNA technology and why is it useful?

DNA technology is the practical application of our knowledge about DNA to solve problems. For example, we might be able to work out if a living thing has been present at a particular place, by sampling the environment to see if any of its DNA has been left behind. Humans and many other animals shed hair or skin as they move around. Scientists have figured out ways of extracting DNA from hair and skin and identifying individuals from their DNA sequences. This is why you will see DNA in news headlines about criminals being caught, when they have left behind 'DNA evidence.'

At this point it might be useful to point out that we do not always do the same kind of DNA test to solve a problem, or answer a question. In the

'Brain' and batteries of the cell

The nucleus acts like the 'brain' of the cell by giving instructions for growth, repair and what to do next. Mitochondria control the flow of energy used by cells. The energy comes from food in animals and from sunlight in plants, with the help of another cell body (which is only found in plants) called the chloroplast. Hundreds of mitochondria are found inside the majority of complex cells. According to the theory of 'endosymbiosis' cell bodies such as mitochondria and chloroplasts were separate organisms billions of years ago but joined up with bigger ones, resulting in new types of organism, including the ancestors of animals and plants.

case of identifying a burglar at a crime scene, a 'DNA fingerprint' is often needed because the aim is to identify an individual. This is not always necessary. For example, I collect water samples from ponds, with the help of volunteers, to check for the presence of a rare animal, called the great crested newt. I have no need to identify individual great crested newts. I am just trying to find out if that particular species of animal lives there, so that I can make sure that its habitat is protected and not destroyed by development.

To do this, all I need is a test that identifies a sequence of DNA that is always present in great crested newts but is not present in any other living thing. This sort of test can also be used to solve wildlife crimes. For instance, people smuggling items illegally made of rhino horn will sometimes try and pretend that they are made of something

Mitochondrial DNA is found in small, circular packets inside the mitochondria. Most cells contain hundreds of mitochondria.

Nuclear DNA is found in the nucleus of the cell, mainly in long, linear packets called chromosomes. Most cells have a nucleus. A few specialised cells (such as red blood cells) do not have a nucleus.

Several of the other structures shown inside the cell are involved in making proteins, under instruction from the nucleolus (the darker area within the nucleus). Items leaving or entering the cell often do so via 'vesicles' in the cell membrane.

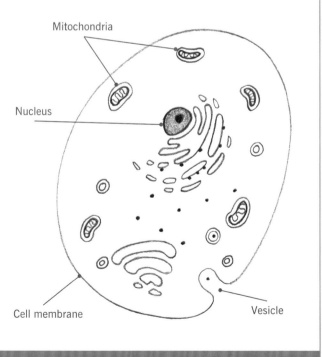

Mitochondria

Nucleus

Cell membrane

Vesicle

Simplified structure of an animal cell

© Pete Minting

legal and more common, such as cow horn. In this book we have focused upon Scottish wildlife but there have been cases in Scotland where people have illegally imported or sold items made from exotic species, such as elephants, rhinos and tigers.

How do you extract DNA from samples and how is it analysed?

In this section, I have provided some basic information about how DNA testing and analysis is done. It is important to point out that scientists usually decide on the questions they are trying to answer before they start doing any DNA testing and the collection of samples needs to be well-planned, because it is easy to waste time and money, if there is not a good plan to begin with.

It is also important to point out that DNA is not evenly distributed within the bodies or cells of organisms. Although the majority of the cells in a human body do contain DNA, it is usually concentrated within two types of cell body that are found within cells. One of these is called the nucleus and the other is called the mitochondrion (plural = mitochondria).

Once you have a set of samples, it will be necessary to extract DNA from them in order to do a DNA analysis. DNA extraction is fairly straightforward, as long as you have well-preserved samples of the organism to work with. You can easily extract DNA from strawberries, using basic equipment found in most school laboratories. Instructions for how to do this are freely available on the internet (for example, see *www.youtube.com/ watch?v=hOpu4iN5Bh4*).

If you grind up a sample from a study organism and extract DNA from it, this will normally contain 'genomic DNA', in other words, all of the DNA that is present in the organism's genome. The genome includes the DNA from the nucleus and mitochondria. There are ways of selectively extracting mitochondrial or nuclear DNA but the extraction process usually produces genomic DNA.

Once you have extracted the DNA from your samples, it is possible to do a huge variety of things with it. A suitable method or 'protocol' is needed to find and read the sequences of DNA that you are interested in. Sometimes scientists sequence the entire genome (as in the Human Genome Project) but this is not usually necessary.

Often it is possible to find answers by analysing a specific part of the genome. In the laboratory, scientists use 'primers' and 'probes' to cut out and pick up the bits of DNA they are interested in. This 'target' DNA is usually copied or 'amplified' several times, to make it easier to detect and read its sequence, or the length of the sequence. Today most of this work can be done by machines, which are rapidly reducing the amount of time it takes to do DNA tests. Development of a DNA protocol is hard work but once it exists, it can be used many times, just like a cake recipe.

You can easily extract DNA from strawberries

Microsatellite DNA – repetitive DNA, found mainly in the nucleus

The study of 'microsatellite' DNA is a popular way of comparing individuals and populations. Microsatellite DNA has nothing to do with satellites or space rockets. It is simply repetitive DNA, where the same short sequence of nucleobase pairs is repeated several times. The most useful or 'informative' microsatellite sequences are usually within nuclear DNA. The number of repeats varies between individuals, which means that a unique DNA fingerprint (also called a DNA profile) for an individual can be generated using microsatellites from several locations within the genome.

If you do not need to identify individuals and only need to identify the type of organism (species) involved, or study the structure of a population, you will need to sequence fewer microsatellites. At the moment, many scientists are starting to use shorter repetitive sequences, called single nucleotide polymorphisms or SNPs (affectionately known as 'snips') as well as microsatellites but the principle remains broadly the same.

Mitochondrial DNA – largely inherited from the mother

I should also explain why so many genetic studies of wildlife and people involve mitochondrial DNA (mtDNA), instead of nuclear DNA. One reason is that there are usually at least 500x more copies of mtDNA than nuclear DNA in a cell, because each cell normally has lots of mitochondria but only one nucleus. Consequently mtDNA is easier to detect in samples from a dead organism that has started to break down, or from an environment where the study or 'target' organism was once present, because

there were so many more copies of it in the first place. The success of DNA work often depends upon the ability to find and artificially copy (amplify) tiny amounts of DNA in samples.

There is another quirk about mtDNA that is important to know. Usually, the majority of mtDNA found in an animal's cells derives from its mother, because male sperm contain few mitochondria, compared to the female egg. Studies of the evolutionary history of animal populations depend heavily upon mtDNA evidence, partly because mtDNA is more easily extracted than nuclear DNA from ancient bones or museum specimens. Because mtDNA is nearly all inherited from the female parent, this evidence is usually 'from the mother' or 'matrilineal' and does not tell us much about the male half of the population. However, mtDNA evidence can help to work out where an animal's ancestors came from, how it interbred with other populations and when it colonised new areas.

Unique sequences called 'mtDNA haplotypes' are often used as a starting point for genetic studies because they can be used to identify groups within species, like the surnames of people in a telephone directory. If we are only interested in people with the surnames Campbell and McLeod, there is no point telephoning (or DNA sequencing) everybody else. If you are just trying to identify a species, the technique used is often called DNA barcoding. It is like the way a scanning machine identifies your shopping. You can often see a digital 'barcode' printed on an item for sale in a shop. Mitochondrial DNA is often used as the biological equivalent of a barcode.

Although mtDNA sequences by themselves are less informative than a huge bank of microsatellites or single nucleotide polymorphisms, sometimes the information they provide is sufficient to answer a broad question and sometimes only mtDNA, not nuclear DNA, can be extracted from old or poor quality samples.

Don't worry, be happy – and be prepared to ask for help!

I have only mentioned a few types of DNA test in this book and I have focused mainly on those which have been used to study wildlife. The science of genetics is so advanced that it is not possible to cover everything here. If you search the internet, you will see many examples of how DNA technology is used and the speed at which machines can do DNA tests is increasing every day.

Genetics has its own highly technical language, so do not be put off if you cannot understand much of it at first. There is probably no-one on Earth who understands all of the terminology and tests that are used in genetics today. Most geneticists work in a specific area of DNA science that they understand well. As part of their job, they frequently have to ask other scientists for help.

How is DNA technology being used to help study or save wildlife in Scotland?

In Scotland, there are several species of wild animal that are now benefiting from the application of DNA technology.

Some of you may already be familiar with this because you entered a competition to help produce the content of this book, either by drawing, painting or writing about some of these animals.

There are individual chapters about these animals, which I hope you will find interesting. In these chapters I have included some basic information about them and at least one example of how DNA technology is being used to study or help them. I have not given much technical detail about the technology used; instead I have tried to focus upon the questions and answers.

In the future, it is likely that DNA technology will be used to help many more vulnerable species that need our help to survive. If you are not already involved in wildlife conservation but you are interested in science and wildlife, you may be able to help by volunteering. Many conservation organisations and universities need help from volunteers to collect information about wildlife and this sometimes includes DNA samples. It is frustrating if the results take a long time to appear, but it is worth bearing in mind that once collected, samples can be stored and in some cases, may be re-analysed, following improvements in DNA technology. The samples that we are collecting today may, in years to come, produce even more interesting and useful results.

IN THE FUTURE, IT IS LIKELY THAT DNA TECHNOLOGY WILL BE USED TO HELP MANY MORE VULNERABLE SPECIES THAT NEED OUR HELP TO SURVIVE. IF YOU ARE NOT ALREADY INVOLVED IN WILDLIFE CONSERVATION BUT YOU ARE INTERESTED IN SCIENCE AND WILDLIFE, YOU MAY BE ABLE TO HELP BY VOLUNTEERING.

01
Scottish wildcat

THE SCOTTISH WILDCAT IS ONE OF SCOTLAND'S MOST FAMOUS ANIMALS. BUT VERY FEW PEOPLE HAVE EVER SEEN A SCOTTISH WILDCAT. THERE ARE TWO MAIN REASONS FOR THIS. FIRSTLY, WILDCATS ARE VERY GOOD AT HIDING AND TEND TO AVOID PEOPLE, ESPECIALLY IN PLACES WHERE PEOPLE HAVE HUNTED OR PERSECUTED THEM. SECONDLY, THERE ARE HARDLY ANY SCOTTISH WILDCATS LEFT – THEY ARE NEARLY EXTINCT.

Most European wildcats have clearly-separated tail markings   © Laurie Campbell

SCOTTISH WILDCATS

by Jack Matthew Findlay, Troqueer Primary School, Dumfries

"The Scottish wildcat looks a bit like a domestic cat but they're not the cuddly thing you might play with and I certainly wouldn't be trying. Until the 1950s, they were believed to be mankillers. This isn't true but they are the perfect hunter; intelligent, resourceful, patient, agile and powerful. They have immensely strong thigh muscles which means that they can sprint at a whopping 30mph to outrun their prey. Another feature that makes them superb predators are their eighteen claws, which are really sharp and their flexible wrists, which help with climbing trees."

The Scottish wildcat is really a local population of the European wildcat, which can still be found in several other countries in mainland Europe but it is declining in number across most of its range.

Ancient history of the European wildcat

The European wildcat and the domestic cat are both thought to have descended from populations of the African wildcat. The European wildcat is thought to have been present in Europe for at least 130,000 years (perhaps as much as 200,000 years), after its ancestors moved north and split naturally from African wildcats. In contrast, DNA evidence suggests that domestic cats split from African wildcats quite recently, possibly only 4,000 – 10,000 years ago, when they were domesticated by people in countries near to the eastern end of the Mediterranean Sea.

European wildcats, domestic cats and African wildcats are quite similar in appearance and behaviour. They are closely related and capable of interbreeding (hybridising) and producing fertile offspring. Despite their similarity and ability to interbreed, they have recently been classified as three separate species.

DNA evidence suggests that European wildcats survived in three places in Europe during the peak of the last ice age 25,000 years ago; in Iberia (Spain and Portugal), southern Italy and parts of the Balkans (mainly in Croatia and Slovenia). After the last ice age ended, European wildcats were able to recolonise much of northern Europe, including what is now Britain, by 12,000 – 15,000 years ago (before the expansion of the English Channel split Britain from mainland Europe 8,500 years ago).

The recent history of wildcats and domestic cats in Britain

The European wildcats that naturally colonised Britain (including Scotland) were probably isolated from other closely-related cats for about 10,000 years, until domestic cats were brought to Britain by people. There are records of Roman people bringing domestic cats to Britain about 2,000 years ago but they may have been introduced even earlier, perhaps 3,500 years ago. Since then, European wildcats have probably been hybridising with domestic cats in Britain. Wildcats are now extinct in England and Wales (but they may have been present in northern England until the 1700s).

A few European wildcats still exist in Scotland, where they are known locally as Scottish wildcats. They used to be fairly widespread across mainland Scotland but are not thought to have colonised many of the Scottish islands. Some place names may be linked to the Scottish wildcat, such as Cadboll in Sutherland, which means 'hill of the cat, or Catts' and the northern county of Caithness ('headland of the Catts'). The Catts were a Pictish tribe which lived in this area about 1300 years ago. Pictish tribes often had a strong cultural association with a particular wild animal.

The Scottish wildcat has declined for many reasons, including hunting and trapping (often by gamekeepers on shooting estates, who saw them as a threat to gamebirds such as pheasants and grouse), habitat loss (European wildcats do best in a mix of native woodland and grassland, a habitat which is now rare in Scotland), road mortality (traffic has increased hugely since the 1960s), the introduction of disease by domestic pets and hybridisation with domestic cats. The

Scottish wildcat has been protected by the Wildlife and Countryside Act since 1988, so it is illegal to kill them deliberately but it is legal to shoot wild-living domestic cats (feral cats), which can look very similar.

The majority of Scottish wildcats have now hybridised with domestic cats. It is now very difficult to find any wild-living cats in Scotland that are 'pure' Scottish wildcats. Recent surveys (by camera-trapping) suggest that there are only a few places in Scotland with wild populations of cats that look (mainly) like Scottish wildcats. Most of these are near to the Cairngorm mountains but also the Morvern peninsula on the west coast and a few areas near Aberdeen and Inverness.

What does a Scottish wildcat look like?

One of the main problems with designing an identification system for Scottish wildcats is the absence of ancient specimens of this animal that pre-date the arrival of domestic cats in Britain. However, scientists have been able to use museum specimens (bones and

The pelage chart was originally published in: Kitchener A. *et al* (2005) A diagnosis for the Scottish wildcat (*Felis sylvestris*): a tool for conservation action for a critically-endangered felid. Animal Conservation Vol 8: p223–237.

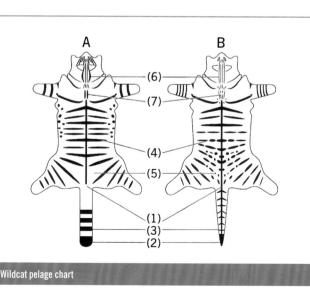

Wildcat pelage chart

'A' is the typical wildcat pattern:

1. Line along back stops at tail base

2. Tail tip is blunt

3. Tail bands are separate

4. Side-stripes are unbroken

5. No spots on hindquarters

6. Thick stripes on back of neck

7. Thick stripes on top of shoulders

Two views of the same Scottish wildcat   © Scottish Wildcat Action   Two views of the same domestic tabby cat   © Pete Minting

stuffed wildcats) and images (drawings, photographs) from Scotland over the last 200 years to work out what a Scottish wildcat 'should' look like, with a reasonable degree of confidence.

The colour and patterning of the fur (pelage) provides some useful clues. The *pelage chart* on page 14 (from Andrew Kitchener et al 2005) can be used to help tell the difference between a domestic tabby cat (which often looks like a wildcat, at first glance) and a Scottish wildcat.

One of the easiest parts of the cat to check is the tail. In a domestic tabby cat, the tail is often ringed by dark bands but these rings are usually fairly narrow and connected along the top by a dark line. In contrast, the tail of a European wildcat (including the Scottish wildcat) is much thicker, with a few wide, dark rings that are not connected along the top by a dark line.

It is hard to tell the difference between a domestic tabby cat and a Scottish wildcat, if you only get a fleeting glimpse as it runs across the road, or jumps over a wall. But if you do manage to get some photographs, these will be very useful for comparing with the pelage chart.

Is captive-breeding the last hope for the Scottish wildcat?

If the Scottish wildcat is to avoid extinction, captive-breeding is probably necessary because they are now so rare. There may be less than 100 cats with a high proportion of wildcat DNA left in the wild in Scotland. Evidence from camera-

Scottish wildcat by Marshall Markham, Drummore Primary School

trapping has been used to help select several 'wildcat conservation priority areas' in Scotland, where conservation effort is currently being focused.

In the wildcat conservation priority areas, wild-living cats are being trapped and assessed. If they have not already been neutered, any feral (wild-living) domestic cats that are trapped are being neutered before they are released. This is to try and reduce the high rate of hybridisation that is (among other factors) driving Scottish wildcats to extinction. There is also a campaign to encourage domestic cat owners in the priority areas to get their cats neutered (so they cannot have kittens).

Wild-living cats captured in the priority areas (and a few other parts of Scotland) are also being assessed using the pelage chart and DNA tests, to see if they can be regarded as Scottish wildcats with a high degree of confidence. Those which score highly on both the pelage chart and DNA tests may be selected for participation in an official programme of captive breeding and reintroduction.

The use of captive-breeding to boost Scottish wildcat populations is controversial. Some people think that efforts should be focused on protecting the last few Scottish wildcats in the wild. Animals can lose their ability to survive in the wild, if they are kept in captivity for too long. There are many 'Scottish wildcats' in zoos and wildlife parks in Britain. Several of these cats have enough wildcat genes for participation in a programme of captive-breeding and reintroduction. But so far, there have been no official, coordinated releases of

Scottish wildcat by Navya Saini, Williamwood High School

FAR FROM HOME

by Gurpreet Kaur, Glasgow

My paws swell with the feast.
The catch easy, the prey gone.
The sun judges my blood stained teeth,
glistening like the snow,
but my conscience is satisfied.
The undergrowth is rough,
holding me criminal for my crimes.
But my ego is stronger.
until the monsters tear my home from
beneath me.

captive-bred wildcats in Scotland.

It can be difficult to find a good release site for captive-bred animals. Wildcats need to be released in areas with sufficient prey (such as small rodents and rabbits) and suitable habitat. They also need to be released in areas where there is a low risk of persecution by people and a low risk of hybridisation with domestic cats. But if these challenges are met, captive-breeding and reintroduction might save the Scottish wildcat from extinction and help to restore its population to a robust and stable size.

Which DNA tests have been used to study wildcats?

Many types of DNA test have been used to study European wildcats, often to try and work out the difference between them and domestic cats but also to see if the 'real' wildcat populations are isolated from each other, or are able to meet and breed.

Microsatellite DNA 'markers' and mitochondrial DNA 'haplotypes' have been used to study wildcats at a European level. DNA evidence suggests the existence of five main, separate populations of European wildcats in mainland Europe. These are found in Iberia (Spain and Portugal), central Europe, Germany, southern Italy and the north-eastern Italian Alps. Unfortunately, Scottish and Hungarian wildcat populations had to be excluded from the conclusions of this study, because their high degree of hybridisation with domestic cats made it difficult to compare them with other groups. But if wildcats from any of these populations were to meet, they could interbreed, despite the fact that they are separated from each other by large distances.

In the five main populations of European wildcats in Europe, the rate of hybridisation with domestic cats was found to be low (only 5–10%). Hybridisation rates are much higher in Scotland. A study 15 years ago

Scottish wildcat by Mia Beattie, Lockerbie Academy

suggested that around 60% of 'Scottish wildcats' were hybrids with domestic cats. In a more recent study by Scottish Natural Heritage in 2014, all of the cats tested were found to be hybrids but a few of them still had mainly wildcat DNA.

A 'new and improved' DNA test is being used (at the RZSS WildGenes laboratory) to assess the cats trapped in the priority areas for wildcat conservation in Scotland. This latest test uses single nucleotide polymorphism (SNP) markers, instead of microsatellite markers which were used in most earlier studies. The DNA from each cat is tested with a panel of 35 SNP markers. Along with the pelage chart, this test should be able to work

out which of the cats have the most wildcat DNA.

Ideally, wild-living cats in Scotland should be assessed with a combination of DNA tests and the pelage chart. Some cats that do not score highly on the pelage chart might have a reasonable amount of wildcat DNA. For example, some black cats might have a lot of wildcat DNA, as black or 'melanistic' colouration can occur naturally in wildcats (but black colouration is much more common in domestic cats). Sometimes it only takes a few genes to affect the fur pattern or colour in a local population of wildcats. These genes can be from a single interbreeding or 'hybridisation event' with a domestic cat, which occurred several generations

A STUDY 15 YEARS AGO SUGGESTED THAT AROUND 60% OF 'SCOTTISH WILDCATS' WERE HYBRIDS WITH DOMESTIC CATS. IN A MORE RECENT STUDY BY SCOTTISH NATURAL HERITAGE IN 2014, ALL OF THE CATS TESTED WERE FOUND TO BE HYBRIDS BUT A FEW OF THEM STILL HAD MAINLY WILDCAT DNA.

A DIARY OF A WILDCAT

by Mila Todd, Monymusk Primary School, Inverurie

Once upon a time there was a Scottish wildcat. He lived in the mountains, in a forest. Here's a story from his diary. My life was perfect (other than those annoying squirrels). Every day I woke up, stretched and got up to find my breakfast. One particular day I was trying to decide if I wanted fish, mice or rabbits when I noticed a stoat-like creature half way up a tree, muttering something to itself. At first I thought it was a squirrel, so my stride turned quickly into a tiptoe (I may be big but a nip from a squirrel is nasty). As I came closer I saw it was too big to be a squirrel. I stopped tiptoeing, I stopped walking and stared at it. Suddenly it jumped down acrobatically doing back-flips and such but after all this it landed face-first with its nose stuck in the ground. I came up to it and asked "what are you?" it replied in a muffled voice "a pine marten".

Scottish wildcat by Deena Lowery, Lockerbie Academy

ago. In theory, it should be possible to gradually dilute the domestic cat genes out of a hybridised population, if further hybridisation is prevented.

Given the long history and high level of hybridisation that has occurred, finding the best cats to enter a captive breeding group will be a challenge. At the moment, scientists are capturing and testing as many wild-living cats as possible, to get an up-to-date assessment of the situation.

In 2014 a new project called Scottish Wildcat Action was started, in an attempt to save the Scottish wildcat from extinction. More details about this project can be seen at: **www.scottishwildcataction.org**

02
Badger

THE BADGER IS A TOUGH AND ADAPTABLE ANIMAL. IT LIVES IN A WIDE VARIETY OF HABITATS, FROM ANCIENT WOODLANDS TO COASTAL SAND DUNES AND EVEN IN CITIES, IF THERE ARE AREAS OF GREEN SPACE, SUCH AS PARKS AND GARDENS. IN THE BRITISH COUNTRYSIDE, BADGERS ARE FOUND IN MOST AREAS WHERE THE GROUND IS SUITABLE FOR BURROWING.

Badger in the moonlight by Katie Cameron, Ardnamurchan High School

Like the fox, the badger has been persecuted by people for several hundred years but it has managed to survive across much of Britain, including most of mainland Scotland.

Badger behaviour

Badgers are highly social and usually live in family groups, of up to 15 individuals. They spend a lot of their time in communal burrows (the communal burrows of badgers are called setts). Badgers come out of their setts to look for food and find mates. They usually wait until dusk before emerging. When they emerge, they often spend a lot of time grooming themselves and each other. If you watch a group of badgers emerging from their sett, you can often hear them snuffling and scratching at their skin, long after it has become too dark to see them.

Grooming reinforces social bonds between members of the group and helps to remove parasites (such as fleas and ticks). A family group of badgers will often use several different setts, occasionally moving between them. This helps them to avoid parasites, which can build up inside burrows and spread disease, if they stay in the same place for too long. Badgers sometimes replace the bedding (such as dry grass) that they drag into their burrows. This may also help to get rid of parasites.

If a sett is being used by badgers, there is usually some evidence of their activity, such as freshly-dug earth, close to their burrow entrances. Badger setts can be huge, with up to 800 metres of burrows. Most of the burrows are less than 1.5 metres below ground; deep enough to avoid frost but shallow enough not to suffer regular flooding. Unlike some other mammals, such as the hedgehog, which go into a deep sleep during winter (hibernation), badgers do not hibernate. They spend longer inside the sett and sleep for longer periods but they remain active on an almost-daily basis.

A group of badgers emerging from their sett at dusk

© Laurie Campbell

Badger by Seanna McNeill, Arbroath Academy

Omnivore or carnivore?

Badgers are able to eat a variety of food, so are often described as 'omnivorous' but about two-thirds of their diet is typically of animal origin. The diet of badgers varies quite a lot, depending on where they live. About half of the diet of badgers that live in the countryside in Britain (including Scotland) is earthworms and other small invertebrates. They also hunt some larger (but not very big) animals, such as frogs and toads, mice, rats, hedgehogs, rabbits and ground-nesting birds and their eggs.

Badgers also eat plant material, including some crops and are fond of nuts and berries. Elder trees are often found close to badger setts. This may be the result of badgers eating elder berries and accidentally bringing the seeds home. Elder seeds can germinate and grow after passing through the guts of many animals. Badgers will eat discarded human food and some of the heaviest badgers have been recorded in towns and cities, where they have probably grown fat on chips and half-eaten kebabs.

Group interactions and breeding

Badgers are territorial and mark out their territories with numerous 'latrines'. These are small pits in the ground, which badgers dig out and fill with their odorous droppings. Badgers have an excellent sense of smell but fairly poor eyesight. Although badgers maintain territories, they need to interact with other badger groups. Adult male badgers enter the territories of other groups to mate with unrelated females. In this way, badgers manage to mix their DNA effectively and avoid inbreeding. Inbreeding often results in genetic problems, if close relatives mate and produce offspring.

Baby badgers are normally born in February or March, in litters of up to six cubs. They can become independent from their mothers at five months of age and breed at just one year old. They can live for up to 15 years but very few badgers live for that long in the wild.

THE EURASIAN BADGER PROBABLY SPLIT AWAY FROM OTHER ASIAN BADGERS ABOUT FIVE MILLION YEARS AGO. FOSSILS SHOW THAT EURASIAN BADGERS HAD COLONISED WESTERN EUROPE BY THREE MILLION YEARS AGO.

Ancient history of the badger

The badger that is found in Britain is called the Eurasian badger. At least three other closely-related 'sub-species' of badger are found in eastern Asia. There are a few other 'true' badgers (such as the honey badger and American badger) but these are less closely-related.

The Eurasian badger probably split away from other Asian badgers about five million years ago. Fossils show that Eurasian badgers had colonised western Europe by three million years ago. The oldest Eurasian badger fossil found in Britain dates from around half a million years ago.

Although badgers were present in Britain at least half a million years ago, they were driven out by cold conditions during the ice ages. The badgers found in Britain today started recolonising northern Europe after the end of the last ice age, about 17,000 years ago. During the ice ages, they survived in a few areas that remained ice-free in southern Europe. DNA evidence suggests only one of these populations survived to produce the badger populations that are present today in western Europe.

Badgers have colonised what is now Britain more than once but they last recolonised this area of land (including Scotland) at some point between 10,000 and 15,000 years ago, before the expansion of the English Channel separated Britain from mainland Europe.

Recent history of the badger

When mainland Britain was largely covered with woodland (from about 10,000 to 7,000 years ago), the badger (like some of the other animals featured in this book, such as the pine marten) would have been widespread and probably fairly abundant. As the human population began to increase in Britain, humans would have started to destroy woodlands and gradually alter the landscape.

The destruction of woodlands for agriculture, firewood and building would have resulted in more open space. But badgers can persist in open landscapes, as long as they can make setts and find food. Badgers were also hunted by prehistoric people for their fur and meat, as badger meat is edible and badger skins and fur can be used to make clothing. But badger populations were able to withstand this hunting, as they breed quite rapidly and the human population in Britain at that time was quite small. Unlike several other large animals (such as the brown bear, lynx, wolf and beaver), badgers never became extinct in Britain as a result of hunting by humans.

Although badgers are still widespread in mainland Britain, including most of Scotland, they are not found on many Scottish islands. A badger jawbone dating from the Bronze Age (4,000 – 3,500 years ago) was found during an archaeological dig on the Outer Hebrides

Badger by Ava Duffy, Greenfaulds High School

but badgers are not thought to be native to these islands. One theory is that Bronze Age people took some dead badgers to the Outer Hebrides on their boats, before they had time to skin or eat them.

The name 'badger' was probably invented in mediaeval times, about 800 – 1,000 years ago. The old English word 'badge' refers to an emblem or symbol. A picture of the striped, black and white face of this animal is still used as an emblem or logo by many organisations today. Another name for the badger is 'brock' which may come from the ancient Celtic word 'broc' which means grey (apart from the head, the upper side of a badger is usually grey).

Badgers are still hunted for food in parts of mainland Europe and although badger meat is not very tasty, they have been hunted during many wars, by people struggling to find food. Badger

persecution increased in Britain in the mid-1500s, when laws were passed to encourage people to kill animals that were thought to damage crops, or attack livestock. Some of these laws, such as the Act for the Preservation of Grayne (1566), were not abolished until 1863.

In 1835, badgers got some protection for the first time in Britain, under the Cruelty to Animals Act. Among other things, this banned 'badger baiting'. This is a cruel 'sport' where dogs are made to fight badgers that have been cornered in their setts, or put in a pen to fight each other. This is the origin of the phrase 'to badger' someone, when the word badger is used as a verb to describe harassment.

Several other laws now help to protect badgers in Britain, including the Badgers Acts (1973 and 1992), the Nature Conservation Act (Scotland) 2004 and the Wildlife and Natural Environment

Bovine TB and badger culling

The killing of badgers has been approved by the government in parts of England on several occasions since 1973 and in parts of Wales since 2015. This 'culling' is being done in specific areas, to try and reduce disease transfer between badgers and cattle. Badgers (along with many other wild and domestic animals) can be infected with a bacterial organism that causes a disease called tuberculosis (TB). The strain of TB that is most commonly detected in cattle and wildlife near to cattle farms is called bovine TB. Badgers often live on or next to farmland and are often infected with bovine TB.

At the time of writing this book, badgers were being legally killed ('culled') at several locations in England and Wales, to try and reduce the rate of bovine TB infection in cattle. Farmers lose money as a result of bovine TB, as infected cattle (in Britain) must be put down and cannot be sold.

Scientific research suggests that the badger culls may not work. Badger culling can actually increase infection rates in cattle near to where the culls take place, possibly because badgers are stressed by culling. When their families are broken up, survivors travel into other areas and they are more likely to become ill and transmit TB, because stress affects their immune systems and they cannot fight back against the bacteria. TB often lies 'dormant' in animals that are well-fed and not stressed, including many humans that have TB but do not know that they are infected.

Scotland is often described as 'free' of bovine TB but this is not actually true. It just means that the rate of bovine TB infection in cattle is fairly low. There has been no culling of badgers in Scotland to try and reduce bovine TB in cattle. Cattle are regularly transported across Britain and the tests for bovine TB are not 100% reliable, so it would be surprising if Scotland was free of bovine TB.

Other methods might help to reduce the impact of bovine TB on livestock and wildlife. Vaccination against TB can often prevent infection but it does not remove TB from animals that are already infected. Vaccination costs money and farmers and farming organisations usually argue against solutions which add to the cost of farming. And although cattle can be easily captured and vaccinated, it is difficult to capture and vaccinate a high proportion of the badger population.

IT IS NOW ILLEGAL (IN SCOTLAND AND THE REST OF BRITAIN) TO DELIBERATELY KILL OR INJURE A BADGER, INTERFERE WITH A BADGER SETT, OR POSSESS OR SELL A LIVE BADGER, UNLESS YOU HAVE A GOVERNMENT LICENCE TO DO SO.

(Scotland) Act 2011. It is now illegal (in Scotland and the rest of Britain) to deliberately kill or injure a badger, interfere with a badger sett, or possess or sell a live badger, unless you have a government licence to do so. However, it is legal to possess a dead badger or parts of it, such as its fur or bones, if it was not illegally killed (for instance, from a badger accidentally killed by traffic on a road).

In the early 1900s, badger numbers in Britain were much lower than they are today, largely because of intensive persecution by farmers and landowners who employed gamekeepers. In the early 1900s there were about 23,000 gamekeepers in Britain but this number declined during the first world war (1914–1918). Since then, badger numbers in Britain appear to have slowly increased. It is difficult to accurately work out the size of a badger population without frequent and expensive surveys but in 2009, there were thought to be around 9,000 family groups of badgers in Scotland and at least 300,000 individual badgers across Britain as a whole.

Despite their wide distribution and relative abundance compared to most other species featured in this book, the majority of people in Britain, including Scotland, have never seen a live badger. Badgers are often killed by road traffic;

BADGERS HUNT AND EAT MICE, RATS AND OTHER SMALL ANIMALS THAT DAMAGE CROPS, SUCH AS BEETLES AND SLUGS, SO ALTHOUGH THEY EAT SOME CROPS THEMSELVES (AND SOMETIMES DIG UP BULBS IN PEOPLE'S GARDENS), THEY MAY HAVE POSITIVE EFFECTS ON CROPS THAT HAVE NOT BEEN RECOGNISED.

in fact, this is the most common cause of death for adult badgers in Europe today, including Britain. Although few people have seen a live badger, dead badgers can often be seen lying on or next to roads. Unfortunately badgers (like many other wild animals) have not had time to evolve a safe way of crossing roads. In some countries, wildlife tunnels and bridges are constructed to allow wildlife to cross roads safely but this is rare in Scotland.

Do you like badgers?

The manufacturers of Marmite have run advertisements suggesting that most people either hate or love Marmite. It is a bit like that with badgers. Long before they were blamed for the spread of bovine TB, badgers were disliked by farmers and landowners for raiding livestock pens (especially chicken houses and pheasant pens) and causing crop damage. Most modern chicken farms have badger-proof buildings but badgers are still disliked by many farmers and landowners. Badgers often enter cattle sheds at night and steal food from cattle troughs, because unlike most chicken farm buildings, most modern cattle sheds are still not badger-proof.

Many other people regard badgers as endearing creatures. They appear as fictional characters with positive qualities in many stories, including The

Wind in the Willows, The Chronicles of Narnia, The Animals of Farthing Wood and The Fantastic Mr Fox. The badger is also the emblem of Hufflepuff house at Hogwarts School, in Harry Potter. Hufflepuff pupils are quiet but brave and willing to stand up for themselves and fight back if threatened, just like real badgers.

Real badgers also hunt and eat mice, rats and other small animals that damage crops, such as beetles and slugs, so although they eat some crops themselves (and sometimes dig up bulbs in people's gardens), they may have positive effects on crops that have not been recognised.

Fox hunting and badger baiting

The hunting of wild animals for 'sport' affects badgers in several ways. Badgers and foxes often use the same burrows to hide in. Badgers have very strong front legs and claws, which they use to dig burrows but foxes are not very good at digging. Consequently, foxes often use empty badger setts, rather than trying to dig their own burrows. Although it has been illegal to deliberately hunt badgers with dogs in Britain since 1835 and the hunting and killing of foxes by dogs was banned in Scotland in 2002 (and in England and Wales in 2004), it is still legal to flush a fox out of a burrow using dogs and then shoot it. As you can probably imagine, this means that badgers are still disturbed by fox hunting because it is difficult to tell which animals are in a burrow, before hunting begins.

As part of fox hunting, it used to be common practice to block the entrances to badger setts (sometimes for several days) to prevent foxes entering. This had bad effects on badgers, for example if they suffocated, or could not leave their burrows to find food. It is now illegal to

Badgers use their excellent sense of smell to find food © Laurie Campbell

interfere with a badger sett, so if you see any evidence of setts being blocked or dug up, contact the police.

Although badger baiting has been illegal since 1835, it still happens today. People involved in badger baiting are often involved in other forms of violent crime. Badgers are often dug out of their setts by badger-baiters using spades. Badgers in remote or wooded places are more vulnerable to attack, because people can spend more time digging them out without being caught.

If captured or cornered, a badger is able to fight back because it has very strong jaws, sharp teeth and loose skin on its body, which means it can still twist and turn if bitten and gripped by another large animal, such as a dog. These features may have evolved as defences against natural predators of the badger, such as wolves and bears (which are now extinct in Britain). People who do badger baiting often place bets on whether their dog will win a fight against a badger. Often the

badger or dog dies, as a result of the injuries caused by fighting.

DNA and badger baiting

In 2016, three men in Yorkshire, England were sent to prison for deliberately injuring a badger (against the Badger Act 1992) and causing suffering to their own dogs, as a result of badger baiting. No badger body was found in this case but bloodstains on the clothes of the men and hair from the teeth of one of their dogs tested positive for badger DNA. The DNA tests were carried out by the Science and Advice for Agriculture Laboratory (SASA) in Edinburgh. Despite the lack of a body, the DNA evidence was strong enough to convict the men, jail them and ban them from keeping dogs.

DNA evidence is playing an increasingly-important role in solving wildlife crimes and several other groups of badger-baiters have now been convicted in the same way (mainly in England but badger baiting also happens

Badger hair caught on barbed wire © Laurie Campbell

in Scotland). Although badgers are probably not at risk of extinction as a result of badger-baiting in Britain, the suffering caused to the animals involved is horrendous. Most people agree that unnecessary cruelty to animals for the sake of entertainment should be prevented.

How many badgers are there? Do badgers visit other groups?

Scientists are finding out more about badger populations in the wild by doing DNA tests on samples of badger poo and hair. Badger hairs are often caught on barbed wire. These tests are usually done on parts of the DNA that are easily located and repetitive ('microsatellite' DNA) but which differ slightly between individuals and families. If a large 'panel' of microsatellites is tested, individual badgers can be identified.

If lots of samples are collected, it is often possible to identify individual badgers that have been missed by other survey techniques. It can be difficult to work out which of the badgers are part of the local family group, or are just occasional visitors. However, this is a very promising area of research which will improve the accuracy of badger

surveys and probably reveal more about how different families of badgers interact with each other.

Is the badger a bear? No, it's stoatally different...

DNA technology has also been used to help investigate the ancient history of badgers and work out how closely-related they are to other animals. One of the first zoologists, Linnaeus, thought that the badger was a type of bear, based on its stocky shape and behaviour. Some animals also display similar social behaviour to badgers, grooming each other and spending a lot of time in communal burrows (such as meerkats). But badgers, bears and meerkats are not very closely related, despite being in the same broad group of mammals called Carnivora. The last common ancestor of all the Carnivora probably lived at least 40 million years ago. Bears are in their own family, meerkats are in a family that includes cats and hyaenas and badgers belong to a family called 'mustelids' which includes stoats, polecats, otters and martens (such as the pine marten).

DNA evidence has recently confirmed that the stink badgers of south-east Asia are not 'true' badgers at all but instead belong to the same mammal family as skunks. Similarities between the appearance or behaviour of animals do not always guarantee that they are closely-related.

More information about work being done to help badgers in Scotland can be found at: www.scottishbadgers.org.uk

The Collins New Naturalist book *Badger* by Tim Roper (2010) also contains lots of interesting information. This book is currently expensive to buy but you may be able to borrow a copy from your local library. The ISBN number is: **9780007320417**.

03
Pine marten

FEW ANIMALS CAN COMPETE WITH THE PINE MARTEN, WHEN IT COMES TO CLIMBING. IF YOU SEE ONE DURING THE DAY, YOU MAY BE TREATED TO A SPECTACULAR DISPLAY AS IT LEAPS FROM TREE TO TREE IN PURSUIT OF A SQUIRREL.

◻

PINE MARTENS ARE MAINLY CARNIVOROUS (THEY USUALLY EAT OTHER ANIMALS) BUT THEY ALSO LIKE TO EAT NUTS AND BERRIES.

Pine martens are from the same family of mammals as badgers, stoats and otters but unlike these animals, they are specialised climbers. They prefer to sleep and nest (or 'den') high up in hollow trees. They are often difficult to spot during the day, as they tend to wait until it is dark before coming down to the ground. Although few people have seen a pine marten, they are now present in most of mainland Scotland, outside of large towns and cities.

In the early 1900s, pine martens were very rare in Britain and north-west Scotland was one of the few places where they survived. They are now legally protected and have recolonised many areas. They have also been reintroduced to southern Scotland and Wales. An increase in the amount of land covered by trees has helped, although much of this is commercial forestry, which is not ideal habitat, largely because it consists almost entirely of young trees. Forestry is more useful for pine martens if some of the trees are left to grow old, or if den boxes are provided. When hollows develop in old trees, these are very useful for wildlife, including nesting birds and pine martens (and other animals which are

typically considered less 'cute' such as bats, insects and spiders!).

Pine martens are mainly carnivorous (they usually eat other animals) but they also like to eat nuts and berries. Recently it has been suggested that pine martens are helping to prevent the spread of the grey squirrel (a non-native, North American species) in Britain, including Scotland. The grey squirrel is bad news for British wildlife, because it carries diseases (such as squirrel pox) and competes with native red squirrels for food. Grey squirrels have been disappearing from many areas recolonised by pine martens. The reasons for this are not yet clear but pine martens might be able to catch and kill grey squirrels more easily than red squirrels.

Pine martens also prey on birds and their eggs. They will raid birds nests on the ground and in trees, if they can get to them. Their tendency to climb into chicken and pheasant cages in search of food has made them unpopular with gamekeepers, who frequently poisoned, trapped or shot them until this became illegal in 1981. Recently gamekeepers have argued that pine martens should lose their protected status, following

Pine martens are very well-adapted for climbing trees
© Robert Cruickshanks

their recent recovery and the fact that they sometimes prey on other protected species, such as the capercaillie (one of Scotland's rarest birds). However, it should be possible for these species to live alongside each other, given that they are both native species and co-existed in Scotland for thousands of years before human activities resulted in their decline.

Some people dislike the pine marten for its predatory behaviour but it is very popular with people on wildlife-watching holidays. Wildlife tourism companies often put out bait for pine martens at feeding stations, so that people can see them. Pine martens have a liking for jam sandwiches but this is probably not good for their teeth. The pine marten is mainly chocolate-brown with a long fluffy tail,

sub-species of marten which exist today. In mainland Europe, the closely-related beech marten sometimes lives in the same forests as the pine marten.

European pine martens colonised what is now Britain from mainland Europe about 12,000 years ago, just after the last ice age. As with many other land animals, they managed to do this before the expansion of the English Channel separated Britain from mainland Europe. When Britain, including Scotland, was largely covered in forest (10,000 to 7,000 years ago), the pine marten was very common and widespread but once humans began to remove a lot of woodland from the landscape, their numbers began to decline. Although it is quite small (about the same length but slimmer than a domestic cat), the pine marten was also hunted and trapped for its high-quality fur.

The combination of habitat loss and deliberate persecution by humans led to the near-extinction of the pine marten in Britain by the early 1900s. A few small populations survived in the Highlands of Scotland and a few may have survived in parts of northern England and Wales.

cream-coloured 'bib' and pale-bordered ears. When running on the ground or across a road, it can look like a small fox but unlike a fox, it can run up and down trees at high speed.

Pine martens in Britain

The ancient, evolutionary history of the pine marten is quite complicated and there are still many other species and

MR 'N' MRS MARTES

by Leah Stanley, St Joseph's Academy, Kilmarnock

Mr 'n' Mrs Martes,
wi' thair fowk o'five.
Up heich in th' trees,
Is whaur thay wull thrive.

Up in Fort uilleum
In a nook in a tree.
Sloching the bilberries,
Bit fur weans thay hae three.

Mrs Martes wis up th'duff,
Born in the drockit days.
Three kits popped oot,
Mack, Maggie 'n' Maize.

Mirk broon in colour,
wi' a pale yella bib.
Dinnae hauup me?
Tis na fib!

Thay hu thair tea at four,
In th' mournin' ah mean.
Blaeberries, voles 'n' carrion,
Fairn fit fur th' Queen.

Kip in th' day,
up in th' nicht.
Think ye saw yin in summer?
Aye ye be richt.

Noo this is pure weird
Thair jobby is blue.
Tae mony bilberries,
Isnae guid fir you.

An' if ye see wan,
Dittering aboot
Don't touch him!
He'll gi' ye a boot!

Pine marten dropping or 'scat'   © Lizzie Croose

DNA studies of pine martens

DNA testing has been used to answer two main questions with regard to pine martens in Britain. Firstly, what is the recent history of pine marten populations in Britain? Did they really go extinct in England and Wales, as some people have suggested? Secondly, where do pine martens exist in the wild in Britain today? Several reports of pine martens in parts of Britain where they have not been seen for at least a hundred years have been investigated with the help of DNA tests.

To investigate the recent history of pine martens in Britain, scientists have been comparing DNA from pine marten bones in museums with new samples collected from the wild. Samples can be collected from wild pine martens in a number of ways, including from dead pine martens killed by traffic, hair samples from 'fur snagging' devices at feeding stations and from pine marten 'scats' (droppings). Pine martens are difficult to find during the day but it can be easy to find their scats, as they often leave them on forest tracks, to mark their territory. However, their scats can look similar to those of other animals, so a DNA test is needed to confirm they are

Camera-trapping is also a good way to detect pine martens © Pete Minting

ancestors and where it came from).

It is important to point out that DNA analysis is just one method of studying animals and it is not always reliable. Sometimes pine marten scats do not test positive (these are called 'false negatives') if the DNA has broken down. Other modern technologies, particularly camera-traps, can be just as useful for detecting pine martens and many other animals which are shy and largely active at night.

from pine martens. The test checks for a 315 base-pair sequence of mitochondrial DNA that is only found in pine martens. If the scat sample is of good quality, it can also be used to work out the mitochondrial 'haplotype' of the animal (which can provide information about its

What does the evidence show?

The DNA results from a study in 2012 support the idea that pine martens did go extinct in England and Wales. DNA samples taken from pine marten bones in museums show that the original English and Welsh populations had a different DNA sequence (mitochondrial haplotype i) to those now living in the

Pine marten by Rachel Simpson, Arbroath Academy

THE "SURVIVAL"

by Christopher Queen, St Joseph's Academy, Kilmarnock

Pine martens rarely dare to go down to the forest floor. Or certainly not in these woods. So, for this one pine marten to come out of the shelter of the trees, never mind on to the forest floor, was big news in the pine marten colony. Why was it such a big deal?

On the forest floor lived a family of red foxes, the kings of the woods - it was their territory, and theirs alone. So why did he dare to come down? Deep in the forest, just outside the cave that the foxes lived in, was the berry bush. With the foxes dominating the forest, food was hard to come by. Every pine marten craved those lovely berries.

It was the 13th July, deep in summer. The sun was beating down on the pine marten's back, like he was in a desert. This pine marten was very young. For the first time in his life he peered down at the forest floor. Grass as green as emeralds and a sea of brown, crisp leaves flooded the forest floor.

The pine marten wondered what was so bad about it. He jumped down onto the ground. The leaves felt great under his feet. He scrunched his toes up and felt the crisp golden leaves crumple up under them. It was lovely! Surely it was safe down here? Nothing could go wrong... could it?

wild in England and Wales. Today, the majority of pine martens in England and Wales have mitochondrial haplotype a, which is much more typical of Scottish pine martens. This might be the result of unofficial reintroductions (or natural recolonisation from Scotland, in the case of northern England) but more work is needed to figure out the whole story.

As explained elsewhere in this book, mitochondrial DNA does not tell us much about the male ancestors of an animal, because it is inherited largely from the mother. Male pine martens have been recorded moving tens of kilometres (further than females) and it is possible that some have dispersed even further, without any human assistance. Future studies using nuclear DNA could help to work out what has been happening in greater detail.

Where do pine martens exist in the wild today in Britain?

A recent survey of pine martens in Scotland in 2013 suggests that they have significantly expanded their range since the last major survey in the 1990s. New populations were found in many areas. Most of these were detected by the DNA testing of scats.

Much of the expansion of the range of the pine marten in Scotland is thought to have occurred naturally. In addition to its long-standing stronghold of north-western (mainland) Scotland, the pine marten is now found across much of the north-east (including Caithness, Morayshire, Deeside and Aberdeenshire) and many parts of central Scotland, including Perthshire, Tayside and Stirlingshire. There are also a few populations in Angus and Fife.

Pine martens have also recently

Pine marten   © Robert Cruickshanks

colonised two of the largest islands in Scotland, Mull and Skye, where they have not been previously recorded. They may have simply walked onto Skye, via the road bridge which connected Skye to mainland Scotland in 1995. Pine martens were not officially introduced to Mull but human assistance seems likely, given that there is no bridge to Mull and

pine martens are not keen on swimming. It might be possible to work out where the pine martens on Mull came from, by comparing their DNA with that of other pine marten populations.

Pine martens can also be found in southern Scotland, in Dumfries and Galloway and the Borders. They were officially reintroduced to the Glen Trool

Pine marten by Christina Matheson, Sgoil nan Loch

IN WALES, PINE MARTENS FROM SCOTLAND ARE BEING RELEASED BY THE VINCENT WILDLIFE TRUST AS PART OF A REINTRODUCTION PROGRAMME. HAIR SAMPLES ARE BEING TAKEN FROM THESE ANIMALS, SO THAT THEIR DNA IS ON FILE FOR FUTURE STUDIES.

area in the 1980s. Some pine martens from southern Scotland may have moved south and recolonised parts of northern England.

In 2010, DNA testing of scats confirmed the presence of pine martens in Northumberland in northern England, followed by Cumbria in 2011 (although sightings had been reported from both of these counties for several years). In 2017 a pine marten was also found dead on a road in Northumberland. These pine martens might be from tiny 'relict' populations that never went extinct, they could have been secretly (and illegally) reintroduced, or they could have recolonised northern England naturally from Scotland.

Several 'official' reintroductions of pine martens have been carried out in Scotland and Wales but several unofficial releases and escapes may also have taken place. DNA evidence suggests that some wild-living pine martens in England and Wales have escaped or been released from private collections. DNA tests of captive pine martens in British zoos, wildlife parks and private collections show that many of these originate from mainland Europe, so they may not be the best source of animals for reintroduction projects in Britain.

Locally-sourced animals are often used for reintroduction projects, to minimise the risk of disease transfer and ensure that the animals are well-suited to their new environment. Many of the behaviours and physical characteristics of animals are encoded in their DNA. In Wales, pine martens from Scotland are being released by the Vincent Wildlife Trust as part of a reintroduction programme. Hair samples are being taken from these animals, so that their DNA is on file for future studies. It should be possible to compare these stored DNA samples with samples found in the wild. This could help to provide a wide variety of information, such as which individuals have survived, where they have moved to and whether they have produced any offspring.

04
Beaver

MOST OF THE BEAVER'S RELATIVES (IN THE MAMMAL FAMILY CALLED RODENTS) ARE QUITE SMALL, SUCH AS MICE, RATS AND SQUIRRELS. BUT BEAVERS CAN WEIGH UP TO 30 KG, THE SAME AS A LABRADOR DOG. ONLY ONE RODENT IN THE WORLD IS BIGGER (THE CAPYBARA FROM SOUTH AMERICA). BEAVERS LIVE ALONGSIDE RIVERS AND LAKES AND SPEND A LOT OF TIME IN THE WATER, SO ARE DESCRIBED AS 'SEMI-AQUATIC.'

A STRIKING FEATURE OF THE BEAVER IS ITS LARGE FRONT TEETH.
THE BEAVER USES THESE RAZOR-SHARP TEETH TO CUT DOWN TREES
WHICH IT USES TO HELP MAKE A 'BEAVER LODGE' OUT OF LOGS, MUD
AND LEAVES.

Like the European otter, which you may also see in rivers and lakes in Europe, the beaver has brown fur. However, the beaver is much more stocky with a broad flat tail, whereas the otter has a thin tail. A beaver will slap the water with its tail if it feels threatened and dive below the surface to hide and escape.

Another striking feature of the beaver is its large front teeth. The beaver uses these razor-sharp teeth to cut down trees which it uses to help make a 'beaver lodge' out of logs, mud and leaves. The lodge is used as a hiding-place or 'refuge' from predators and as a place to store food, particularly during the winter. Beavers will often partly dam the river, or outflow from the lake where they are living. This raises the water level, so that the lodge's entrance is submerged and inaccessible to large predators, such as bears and wolves. Beavers, like most other rodents, are herbivorous. They eat a variety of plants found near the water's edge, plus the leaves and branches of trees that they use for lodge-making. They cut down small or medium-sized trees, including willow, aspen, birch and alder. Trees cut down by beavers often look like giant sharpened pencils.

Female beavers give birth to their young inside the lodge, where they feed on their mother's milk until they are old enough to start feeding on vegetation. Beavers can breed from the age of three and breeding females give birth to litters of 1–6 young, which are called 'kits'. If beavers are in suitable habitat with plenty of food, their population size can increase quite quickly, if there are not many predators and they are not being hunted by humans.

Rare rodent makes a run for it

The only beaver I have seen in Scotland came crashing through the undergrowth and down a river bank into the water, just after sunset. They sometimes make 'mud-slides' down river banks, which they use as a rapid escape route into the water. I had been working there with a group of people earlier in the day and came back to look for a coat that someone had left behind. The beaver was not expecting us to come back and had come out of its dam. Beavers are mainly active at night. I did not know that there were beavers at this site, so I was just as surprised as the beaver!

The ancient history of beavers

There are only two species of beaver in the world today, the North American beaver and the European (or Eurasian) beaver. Five million years ago, there were many other species of beaver, and

European beaver   © Laurie Campbell

a giant species of beaver (as big as a lion) existed until 10,000 years ago in North America. The North American beaver and European beaver have a fairly recent common ancestor but have been separated from each other for at least 7.5 million years.

The distribution of beavers has been strongly affected by several ice ages over the last 120,000 years. During the peak of the last ice age 25,000 years ago, beavers survived in at least three widely-separated places in Europe but they met up again after the climate warmed and the ice sheets, which had covered most of northern Europe, finally melted. European beavers were then able to move back north and recolonise many areas. They recolonised what is now Britain about 12,000 years ago, before expansion of the English Channel separated Britain from mainland Europe.

Birch trees cut down by beavers
© Laurie Campbell

Beavers are thought to have become extinct in Britain by the 1600s.

Recent history of beavers in mainland Europe and Scotland

By the early 1900s, the beaver was virtually extinct in Europe, with tiny populations clinging on in just five countries. Hunting and habitat loss had reduced the size of the remaining populations to less than 300 individuals, possibly below the size needed for a mammal population to stay healthy. In 1922, the first reintroduction of beavers in Europe took place, when beavers from Telemark in Norway (one of the few places where they had survived) were moved to Sweden. Hundreds of reintroductions have now taken place across mainland Europe and beaver numbers have recovered dramatically. Today there are at least 600,000 beavers in Europe, all descended from just a few hundred survivors (this is an example of what scientists call a 'population bottleneck').

In Scotland, there are two places where beavers have become re-established, about 400 years after they became extinct in Britain. One of these populations is in western Scotland, at Knapdale in Argyll. Here beavers were first released in 2009 as part of an official reintroduction project. The other population is in eastern Scotland (Tayside). The Tayside population (in Perthshire and Angus) is not the result of an official project. They may have been deliberately introduced here (illegally, without permission), or they may have escaped from a private collection or wildlife park.

The Knapdale beaver reintroduction has been closely managed from the start. It took many years to design the project and get permission from the

It is possible to find beaver remains in peat bogs that formed in Britain during or after this time and ancient beaver bones have been found in several places. At Ardrossan in Scotland, beaver bones were also found in a 'midden' of discarded shells and other food debris left by ancient people.

For thousands of years before the invention of modern fabrics, beaver fur was highly sought after for the making of clothes. Beavers were also hunted for their meat and 'castoreum' an aromatic secretion which beavers use to mark their territory (still used by some people in 'traditional' medicines and perfumes).

Beaver by Lewis McCulloch, Inverarary Primary School, Argyll

THE BEAVER WAS A POPULAR SUBJECT FOR CHILDREN WHO ENTERED THE COMPETITION TO ILLUSTRATE THIS BOOK AND CHILDREN OFTEN SHOW A POSITIVE RESPONSE TO THE IDEA OF REINTRODUCING EXTINCT SPECIES. THIS ILLUSTRATION, BY LEWIS McCULLOCH, AGED NINE, WON FIRST PRIZE IN THE P4–P5 CATEGORY.

Scottish government. The first beavers released in Knapdale were brought from Telemark in Norway. This was partly because conditions in Norway are similar to Scotland in terms of habitat and climate. It is also because a study of ancient beaver bones from Britain suggested they were similar to those of beavers from Norway. However, there is not a great deal of difference between the bones of beavers from various parts of Europe and some of the skulls of ancient beavers from Scotland are very similar to those of beavers from France.

DNA science and the future of beaver management in Scotland

By analysing the DNA of beavers, scientists have been able to answer several questions that needed to be answered in order to make decisions about beaver management in Scotland. Firstly, where did the beavers in the Tayside area come from? If they were the non-native North American species, the Scottish government would probably have demanded that they be trapped and removed. It is not a good idea to introduce non-native species, for a variety of reasons. Often this can result in the spread of infectious diseases and non-native animals can have unexpected

NORTH AMERICAN AND EUROPEAN BEAVERS DO NOT APPEAR TO BE ABLE TO BREED WITH EACH OTHER AND ARE REGARDED AS DIFFERENT SPECIES. THIS IS PROBABLY BECAUSE THEY HAVE EVOLVED AND CHANGED SLIGHTLY SINCE THEY BECAME SEPARATE POPULATIONS, ABOUT 7.5 MILLION YEARS AGO.

effects on the environment they are moved to, if they behave differently or if they breed or 'hybridise' with other animals that they have never bred with before.

Secondly, if more official releases of beavers are to take place in Scotland, where should they come from? Are the beavers from Norway at Knapdale 'genetically diverse' enough to establish a healthy population? Since the beginning of the official reintroduction project, more evidence has come to light about the effects of inbreeding (lack of genetic diversity) on beaver populations.

Where did the escaped beavers on Tayside come from?

DNA tests have been carried out to confirm the origin of the escaped beavers on Tayside in Scotland. Firstly, tests were done to find out if they were European or North American beavers. This was done by reading sequences from the 16S rRNA gene, which is part of the mitochondrial DNA in most living animals. At position number 1,971 of this gene, the European beaver has a Cytosine (C) nucleobase, whereas the North American beaver has a Thymine (T). All of the beavers from Tayside that were tested had a C instead of a T, so were confirmed to be European.

The results of further DNA tests suggest that the Tayside beavers originate from Bavaria in Germany. This was done by comparing single nucleotide polymorphisms (SNPs) present in the DNA of the escaped beavers with the variety of SNPs found in beavers from across mainland Europe.

North American and European beavers do not appear to be able to breed with each other and are regarded as different species. This is probably because they have evolved (changed slightly) since they became separate populations, about 7.5 million years ago. The nucleus of a cell in a North American beaver only has 40 chromosomes (chromosomes are the packets inside the nucleus which contain the DNA), whereas the nucleus of a cell in a European beaver has 48 chromosomes. This is probably one of the reasons why North American and European beavers can no longer breed with each other.

Which beavers should be reintroduced to Scotland?

When reintroducing an animal, it is useful to assess the genetic diversity of the animals brought in, because populations of animals with lots of variation in their DNA sequences, or

Bavarian beaver with ear tags, released at Knapdale in 2017   © Sian Addison, RZSS

'genomes' are more likely to be able to survive infectious diseases, or adapt rapidly to a new environment. In a genetically diverse population, the young animals produced by breeding will be more variable in their physical characteristics, so it is more likely that some of them will survive in a new environment, than if they are all very similar. A lack of variety of DNA in a population also tends to magnify the risk of hereditary (genetic) diseases occurring.

The first beavers officially reintroduced to Scotland came from the Telemark population in Norway that consisted of just 100 individuals, 100 years ago. Today, there are thought to be 170,000 living beavers in Europe which derive from that tiny population (but the population of Norwegian beavers in Scotland has not yet expanded very much). If only three or four families of people founded a city of 170,000 people, it is likely that there

would be a high rate of genetic disease.

Studies of beavers have now shown that in inbred populations, female beavers produce fewer kits than those from populations with greater variation in their DNA. This is one of the reasons why the managers of the official beaver reintroduction project in Scotland are now releasing beavers from other 'source' populations, to ensure that the population is healthy.

Scientists from across Europe have collected DNA samples from living beavers and these have been compared, again using single nucleotide polymorphism (SNP) 'markers'. In this case, a large 'panel' of 306 SNPs was compared. Combined with information from mitochondrial DNA (mtDNA), this information has been used to work out which populations are the most genetically diverse.

Possibly by coincidence, it turns out the Bavarian beaver population in Germany is one of the most diverse in

Europe. DNA evidence shows that the beavers which survived there had a greater variety of ancestors than those in other parts of Europe and have also managed to interbreed with several other beaver populations since numbers began increasing after the 1900s 'bottleneck'. Consequently, Bavarian beavers are now being added to the population at Knapdale, in an effort to boost the diversity of the beaver population in this part of Scotland.

If the beavers in Knapdale and Tayside spread, the two populations may eventually join up and the beaver may again become widespread in Scotland. There are plans to carefully monitor the progress of these populations, including using genetic information to help work out which beavers are most successful, in terms of producing offspring. DNA samples have been collected from all of the beavers that have been officially released, plus quite a few of the escaped Tayside beavers.

STUDIES HAVE SHOWN THAT BEAVERS CAN BOOST THE VARIETY AND ABUNDANCE OF LIFE IN RIVERS AND STREAMS, INCLUDING THE SMALL INSECTS AND OTHER ANIMALS THAT FISH FEED ON. THE FELLING OF TREES REDUCES OVERSHADING, WHICH ALLOWS MORE AQUATIC LIFE TO GROW.

Do beavers have benefits for people and wildlife?

Reintroducing extinct animals is always controversial. People have protested against the reintroduction of the beaver to Scotland for a number of reasons. These include the potential for damage to trees and the flooding of land (caused by beaver dams) that is used for agriculture. However, studies have also shown that beavers can boost the variety and abundance of life in rivers and streams, including the small insects and other animals that fish feed on. The felling of trees reduces overshading, which allows more aquatic life to grow. Amphibians such as frogs benefit from this, because sunlight warms the water and speeds up the growth of tadpoles, so more froglets emerge.

In 2016 the Scottish government gave beavers in Scotland legal protection as a European Protected Species (EPS). Pregnant female beavers and those with young kits (plus the kits themselves) are also protected by animal welfare legislation in Scotland. However, it seems likely that some landowners will apply for licences to remove or kill beavers, if they cause significant flooding on their land.

Much more information about the reintroduction of beavers to Scotland can be found in *Beavers in Scotland, a report to the Scottish Government (2015)* by Scottish Natural Heritage, at: **www.snh.scot/beavers-scotland-report-scottish-government**

More detail about Scottish beaver genetics is also available in SNH report no 682, by the Royal Zoological Society of Scotland (RZSS), at: **www.snh.scot/snh-commissioned-report-682-genetic-assessment-free-living-beavers-and-around-river-tay-catchment**

05
Red deer

THE RED DEER IS THE LARGEST WILD LAND ANIMAL THAT IS FOUND TODAY IN SCOTLAND. IT IS OFTEN DESCRIBED AS 'ICONIC' WHICH MEANS THAT IT IS WELL-KNOWN AND POPULAR. IF YOU GET A POSTCARD FROM SOMEONE ON HOLIDAY IN SCOTLAND, THERE IS A GOOD CHANCE THAT IT WILL BE A PICTURE OF A RED DEER.

Red deer stag with a group of hinds © Laurie Campbell

An adult male red deer is called a stag and the female is called a hind. Only males have antlers, which they use to fight with other males, in order to gain access to a group of females for breeding. The sight and sound of red deer stags fighting and roaring is regarded as a memorable 'wildlife experience' by many people.

Female red deer can breed from the age of two onwards. They usually have one calf per year (young deer can be called a variety of names, including calf, fawn and kid). Young deer depend on their mother's milk, until they are able to feed independently. Red deer are classified as 'herbivores' i.e. plant eaters, although they will sometimes chew on the bones of dead animals to get enough calcium, as this is often a scarce mineral in the places where they live.

The main source of food for an adult deer is vegetation, including grasses and the leaves, stems and bark of shrubs and trees. A large population of grazing animals can have a significant impact on the landscape, by removing the majority of the vegetation.

Red deer are regarded as an important part of Scotland's heritage because they are native to this country but they are also considered of economic value, because many people pay to shoot them and their meat (venison) can be sold. In this country, hunting is largely for 'sport' rather than necessity, as many other sources of meat or protein are available at relatively low-cost.

Large numbers of deer in Scotland are shot to prevent damage to plants. Deer destroy many young trees in commercial forestry and they can also prevent the

Red deer by Owen McKelvey, Leadhills Primary School

recovery of natural woodland. Today there are so many red deer in Scotland that many are also shot to prevent them starving to death in winter, because much of the landscape is so over-grazed that there is not enough good quality vegetation to eat. The desolate landscape of much of northern and western Scotland is partly the result of centuries of over-grazing by livestock (such as sheep and cattle), feral goats and deer.

Deer numbers are very high in Scotland because there are no native predators (apart from humans) that are capable of killing adult red deer. Until it was hunted to extinction in Scotland

about 300 years ago, the European grey wolf would have preyed upon the red deer and limited its population.

How is DNA technology being used to study and protect red deer in Scotland?

There are several ways in which DNA technology has been used, or is being used, to study or help red deer in Scotland. I am going to describe three examples of this work in this chapter.

Firstly, scientists are trying to work out how many red deer in Scotland are really red deer. They could be 'hybrids' or crosses between red deer and other non-native deer species, such as the North American wapiti, or sika deer from south-east Asia. Both wapiti and sika have been released into the wild in Scotland on several occasions since the 1800s. In many cases, wapiti were deliberately introduced by landowners to provide hunters with bigger deer to shoot. Wapiti are bigger than red deer, with bigger antlers and many hunters like to keep the antlers as a trophy.

DEER NUMBERS ARE VERY HIGH IN SCOTLAND BECAUSE THERE ARE NO NATIVE PREDATORS (APART FROM HUMANS) THAT ARE CAPABLE OF KILLING ADULT RED DEER. UNTIL IT WAS HUNTED TO EXTINCTION IN SCOTLAND ABOUT 300 YEARS AGO, THE EUROPEAN GREY WOLF WOULD HAVE PREYED UPON THE RED DEER AND LIMITED ITS POPULATION.

THE CURIOUS LITTLE DEER

by Luke Thomson, Melrose Primary School

Jack was a very curious little deer. But his mother often told him to stay hidden, in a thick shrub inside the forest. Days went by and he did as he was told. Things went on as usual, until one summer afternoon, when Jack's mother still wasn't back after an hour. Jack got worried but at first he stayed put. Another hour passed. By this time he had made up his mind. He left home.

Jack quickly forgot about his mother. He was completely and utterly overwhelmed by the beauty of what he saw. Dainty little flowers of vibrant colours sprouted from the earth. Trees stood proudly with bright green leaves. Golden rays of sunlight shone through the leaves. The occasional hare skipped happily through the grass and a mighty golden eagle cried from above.

Deer calf by Deena Lowery, Lockerbie Academy

Sika were introduced mainly by mistake, when they escaped from deer parks on country estates. Red deer can breed with wapiti or sika but DNA evidence is required to work out how often they do, because it can be very difficult to tell if a deer is a hybrid, just by looking at it.

Secondly, scientists have compared what appears to be native red deer populations across Scotland with others on mainland Europe, to see if they really are native, i.e. they got here by themselves.

Thirdly, forensic scientists who investigate crimes have been using DNA technology to find out where deer meat or 'venison' comes from. Sometimes people lie about where deer meat has come from, especially if they did not get permission to hunt it (poaching).

Hybridisation between red deer, wapiti and sika

Does it really matter, if a red deer is not a 'pure-bred' red deer? Why should we care? Hybridisation is one of the trickiest problems faced by people who are trying to save wildlife, as previously mentioned in the chapter on the Scottish wildcat, which is threatened in a similar way. In order to understand why it is so tricky, we need to look at the process used to decide whether an animal is sufficiently different from another to be regarded as a different type of organism, or 'species.'

For a long time, many scientists have used the 'biological species concept' to decide whether organisms belong to the same species. This is based on whether they can breed with each other and produce 'fertile' offspring, which are themselves capable of breeding and producing more offspring. Combined with the shape, size and appearance of organisms (morphology), this initially

THE RED DEER

by Clara Lawrence, Leadhills Primary School

The red deer walks through the snow
walking to find its fine young doe
Its red silky fur glittering in the frost
Looking for its home, so lost, so lost...
Stumbling around searching for warmth
Searching searching in the north
He finally fell into a deep sleep
Then away the snow began to creep.

Red deer by Anya Jackson, Earlston High School

appeared to be a good way of deciding on divisions between species.

However, there can be reasons why it is worth dividing species further, into sub-species, at least for conservation purposes. For example, a native population of ibex (a type of wild goat) that was found in the Tatra mountains of eastern Europe became extinct when ibex from Turkey and Egypt were brought in to try and boost the size of the ibex population. The Tatran ibex is thought to have died out after this introduction because the next generation of 'hybrid' offspring were born at the coldest time of the year. 'Pure' Tatran ibex gave birth at a warmer time of the year, which protected their young from the cold. Birth-timing may be encoded differently in the DNA of ibex from regions with different climates. Although ibex from Turkey, Egypt and the Tatra mountains looked similar, their hybrid offspring did not survive in the wild. If the Tatran ibex had been classified as a different sub-species, the introduction might not have taken place and it might not have become extinct. Today there are probably more tigers in captivity than in the wild but many captive tigers are hybrids, with parents from different geographic regions. It may not be a good idea to release them into the wild.

For similar reasons, scientists have been collecting evidence to see if red deer are hybridising with wapiti and sika in Scotland. In the latest study, no evidence of wapiti DNA was found in wild Scottish deer populations. The wapiti suffers badly from a parasite (called lung worm) in Scotland and this may be one of the reasons for its disappearance. Although DNA evidence suggests that red deer, sika and wapiti had a common ancestor that lived in central Asia 6 million years ago, the wapiti might not have the genes needed for survival in Scotland today. However, there may still be a few wapiti / red deer hybrids 'on the loose' here, because they did initially hybridise.

The picture is very different for sika. A DNA study in 2009 showed that at one site in Scotland (West Loch Awe in Argyll), 43% of deer shot by the Forestry Commission were hybrids between red deer and sika. At this site, they appear to be 'happily' interbreeding with each other, whereas at most of the sites sampled (so far) there is evidence that

Red deer hind with a young calf © Laurie Campbell

they generally prefer to mate with their own species. If the hybridised deer near Loch Awe spread across Scotland, or if many more 'hybrid swarms' like this occur, 'pure' native Scottish red deer may no longer exist, at least on the mainland. Native red deer on remote islands may not be hybridised but deer can swim several kilometres.

Why does hybridisation matter? It seems unlikely that the deer will suffer, if they are surviving and continuing to reproduce. But the owners of hunting lodges might not be pleased because sika are much smaller than red deer, with smaller antlers. Sika also look different; as well as their lighter build, their fur is much greyer in winter than that of the red deer and they make different sounds. Some people are not worried about red deer / sika hybridisation and do not think that it is worth spending time and money to try and prevent it. However, others believe

Red deer by Saul McGivney, Arbroath Academy

that we should protect, or 'conserve' native species as much as possible. If we do not, some of them may go extinct, or hybridise to the point where they are no longer recognisable as the species which they once were.

When cross-breeding occurs between a male and a female of two different species, the first generation of hybrid offspring are called 'F1' hybrids. This has nothing to do with motor racing, Formula One, or Lewis Hamilton. If an F1 hybrid red deer / sika becomes an adult and breeds with a red deer, the next generation of offspring are regarded as having 'back-crossed' into the red deer population (and are called BC1 instead of F1). If these BC1s also grow up and mate with red deer, the sika genes will be diluted again. Each generation the number of sika genes will have halved (approximately) because when mammals reproduce, the offspring get roughly half of their DNA from their

father and half from their mother. If this dilution kept going, it would get to the point where virtually no sika genes could be detected. However, at any point the process could reverse, or go the other way on day one, so it all depends on what happens in each breeding population.

Is there a solution?

Estate managers and deer stalkers could try and remove as many sika (or at least, deer that look like sika) as possible, by legally shooting them. In some places, installation of deer fencing might also help to limit access of sika to red deer populations. DNA evidence, from mitochondrial DNA which nearly all comes from the female parent, suggests that most F1 red deer/sika hybrids are the result of sika stags mating with red deer hinds, rather than the other way around. Consequently it might be best to concentrate effort on the removal of

Red deer stag (left) and sika stag (right)   © Laurie Campbell

sika stags from wild deer populations in Scotland, if a serious effort is to be made to tackle the threat posed by hybridisation. However, some people will not be happy about the killing of deer, just because they do not happen to be a species of deer that is native to this country. It is not the sika's fault that it was transported to Scotland.

The DNA tests used to study hybridisation between red deer and sika in Scotland

It has been possible to work out the geographic origin of the sika found in Scotland by looking at sections of repetitive DNA found in the cell nucleus (microsatellite DNA), plus mitochondrial DNA (mtDNA). Samples from sika in Scotland were compared with those of

several sika populations in south-east Asia. This suggests that the sika in Scotland originated from the island of Kyushu in Japan. This ties in with records about exports from Japan at the time.

The latest genetic studies carried out to investigate the hybridisation of red deer and sika in Scotland have involved the comparison of a panel of 22 microsatellite 'markers', plus mitochondrial DNA (mtDNA) analysis to confirm the species of the female parent. There is a 39 nucleobase-pair sequence of mtDNA that only occurs once in red deer but is copied several times in sika. When carrying out DNA tests, it is often not necessary to read the actual sequence every time. In this example, because part of the mtDNA is copied several times in sika but not red deer,

IT HAS BEEN POSSIBLE TO WORK OUT THE GEOGRAPHIC ORIGIN OF THE SIKA FOUND IN SCOTLAND BY LOOKING AT SECTIONS OF REPETITIVE DNA FOUND IN THE CELL NUCLEUS (MICROSATELLITE DNA), PLUS MITOCHONDRIAL DNA (mtDNA).

ABOUT A STAG

by Cheryl McIntyre, Ardnamurchan High School

"Look over there, behind the bushes," whispered John, a local poacher.

"What, where? What are we looking at?" replied Jimmy, his son.

"Look at the size of his antlers, worth a lot of money he is !!!"

"What is it, I don't understand, what are we looking at?"

There was a rustling noise coming from behind a bush, John aimed his rifle at the bush and waited.

"This is it, we'll be rich soon, boy!"

"Oh, it's a stag - OK, I get it now," Jimmy muttered.

After a while the stag made a run for it, from behind the bush. John rested his finger on the trigger and took aim... BANG!!!!!

The woods went quiet...

it was only necessary to measure the length of the mtDNA fragments produced to find the answer.

There is often value in carrying out more than one type of DNA test, or increasing the number of sequences analysed. Evidence of hybridisation can be missed, if only a small part of the genome is tested. If hybridisation occurred several generations ago and no more hybridisation has occurred since then, it may be hard to detect, as the hybrid DNA will have been diluted.

The strange genetics of red deer and other animals on Scottish islands

Studies of the genetics of red deer from several Scottish islands have produced some very strange results. For example, DNA evidence suggests that the red deer that used to live on the Orkney islands and those found on the Outer Hebrides probably did not come from Scotland. This mitochondrial DNA evidence came from ancient (mainly bone) samples.

Samples from red deer found across mainland Scotland today, plus recent samples from islands where they still exist, have also produced some interesting results. Most of the results are what we might expect, if red deer had naturally colonised Scotland over land before rising sea levels separated Britain from mainland Europe about 8,500 years ago. However, some of the red deer on the Scottish island of Rum appear to be most closely-related to red deer on the island of Corsica in the Mediterranean Sea, thousands of kilometres away. DNA evidence suggests the red deer on Rum (and Arran) may have been introduced from populations in English deer parks, some of which had a relatively exotic origin. Managers of country estates sometimes transport deer in a similar way to domestic livestock, because it is possible to make money from hunting and selling them.

People have been moving deer (and other animals) for a long time. There is evidence of people transporting deer by sea in southern Europe as early as 20,000 years ago and people are thought to have moved red deer from Scotland to Ireland around 4,000 years ago. Their value as food and for making clothes from deer skins could explain the level of effort used to move them across dangerous seas, in relatively small boats. Red deer do not appear to be the only animals that were transported over large distances to Scotland, thousands of years ago. On the Orkney islands, there is a vole whose closest living relatives are from what is now Belgium and Holland. It may have been accidentally carried with hay used to feed larger animals such as deer but it is also possible that they were deliberately moved, for reasons that we do not yet understand.

DNA profile from deer used to catch poacher for the first time in the UK

In 2015, a poacher was successfully prosecuted and fined for shooting a deer and stealing it from land where he did not have permission to hunt. So far, nothing unusual. People have been killing and stealing deer for food from other people's land in Scotland for hundreds of years. But this was the first time that DNA evidence from a deer had ever been used to prosecute a poacher in the UK.

Following a tip off, police searched a van belonging to a suspected poacher. Inside the back of the van was the body of a red deer (minus its head, lower legs and internal organs). The suspect claimed that he had shot it legally and the police could not prove otherwise, so they could not arrest him. Two days later the internal organs of a red deer were found on ground at Glenfinnan Estate, nearby. The police obtained a search warrant for the suspect's van and collected samples from blood stains that were still present inside the van.

Scientists at Scotland's Science and Advice for Agriculture Laboratory (SASA) in Edinburgh compared the DNA of the blood stains with the DNA of the remains found at Glenfinnan Estate. Detailed DNA profiles were created for both sets of samples (using microsatellite DNA from across the genome). These profiles matched, so it was possible to conclude that the two sets of samples came from the same animal (with a very high level of confidence). This helped to prove (beyond reasonable doubt) that the deer had been illegally hunted without permission at Glenfinnan.

IN 2015, A POACHER WAS SUCCESSFULLY PROSECUTED AND FINED FOR SHOOTING A DEER AND STEALING IT FROM LAND WHERE HE DID NOT HAVE PERMISSION TO HUNT. THIS WAS THE FIRST TIME THAT DNA EVIDENCE FROM A DEER HAD EVER BEEN USED TO PROSECUTE A POACHER IN THE UK.

06
Hare

IF YOU ACCIDENTALLY SCARE A HARE RESTING ON THE GRASS VERGE BY THE SIDE OF A ROAD, IT WILL OFTEN RESPOND BY RUNNING ALONG THE ROAD IN FRONT OF YOU, INSTEAD OF TURNING LEFT OR RIGHT INTO A FIELD. HARES USUALLY RELY ON THEIR ABILITY TO OUTPACE PREDATORS, RATHER THAN CONFRONT THEM. HARES CAN RUN TWICE AS FAST AS HUMANS AND FASTER THAN MOST DOGS. SUPER-FAST MOTOR VEHICLES HAVE ONLY EXISTED FOR ABOUT A HUNDRED YEARS, SO HARES HAVE NOT EVOLVED A DIFFERENT STRATEGY FOR DEALING WITH THEM.

Brown hare in summer © Laurie Campbell

Mountain hare in summer, showing white tail

Mountain hare, with white winter coat

Brown hare in winter by Cameron Glen, Arbroath Academy

THE EUROPEAN RABBIT IS THE ONLY OTHER CLOSE RELATIVE OF HARES THAT IS FOUND IN BRITAIN TODAY. RABBITS LOOK A BIT LIKE HARES BUT THEY ARE MUCH SMALLER.

A tale of two hares (and one rabbit)

There are two species of hare that live in the wild in Britain (including Scotland); the brown hare and the mountain hare. The European rabbit is the only other close relative of hares that is found in Britain today. Rabbits look a bit like hares but they are much smaller.

The brown hare (also known as the European hare) is slightly larger than the mountain hare. The brown hare stays brown all year, whereas the fur of a mountain hare usually turns white in winter. The brown hare also has much longer ears than a mountain hare or rabbit and the top side of its tail is black, whereas rabbits and mountain hares have light brown or white tails.

Source of inspiration

Hares are a very popular subject for artists. If you go into an art or craft shop, you can usually find something with a picture of a hare on it. We received 40 pictures of hares for the competition we organised to help illustrate this book; we have included some of the best entries.

Rabbit clue in Roman stew

Brown hares and European rabbits are not native to Britain, although many people regard them as native, because

Adult European rabbit in Scotland   © Erik Paterson

they have been here for such a long time. One theory is that Roman people introduced them, because rabbit bones have been found among cooking pots at a Roman site in Britain and the first evidence of brown hares in Britain also dates from about 2,000 years ago.

Although rabbits and brown hares can do serious damage to crops, people have introduced them to many places beyond their natural range, because they do well in a variety of open habitats and once established, they can be hunted to provide a useful supply of meat. In the past, rabbit and hare skins were also used to make clothes. The Normans that conquered England in 1066 kept rabbits in large pens and people called 'warreners' looked after them. There are still people with the surname 'Warrener' and 'Warrender' in Britain today, whose ancestors were probably warreners.

In contrast to the brown hare and the rabbit, the mountain hare has been present in northern Britain for at least 12,000 years. It is well-adapted to a cold climate and would have been able to recolonise this land soon after the end of the last ice age, before Britain was separated from the rest of mainland Europe by the expansion of the English Channel about 8,500 years ago.

In Britain, the mountain hare is found mainly in upland areas of Scotland, whereas brown hares and rabbits tend to be found in lowland areas. Brown hares and rabbits are both fairly widespread in lowland Scotland and they have been deliberately introduced to many of the Scottish islands.

Hares and rabbits are herbivorous and eat a wide variety of plants. Their diet usually consists largely of grass but mountain hares can also eat tough

IN THE 1980S IT WAS DISCOVERED THAT MOST OF THE 'BOXING' MATCHES OF HARES ARE ACTUALLY BETWEEN MALES AND FEMALES. A FEMALE WILL 'BOX AWAY' THE MALES, IF SHE IS NOT READY TO MATE.

Brown hares, including a female boxing a male   © Laurie Campbell

I AM NOT A RABBIT

by Iona Dillon, Troqueer Primary School, Dumfries

Long-eared, lanky mammal
Often misunderstood and mistaken
For your smaller family replica, the rabbit
you are far superior
with your powerful hind legs
Reaching speeds of over 40 miles per hour
To outrun the poachers

your fluffy pom pom tail makes you seem innocent
you are a victim yourself
Poachers hunt you
you are a delicacy
A tasty treat to eat
you make a fine stew!

why don't they realise that we are all living creatures
who deserve a happy life
And to live free?

shrubs such as heather. Brown hares and rabbits will also take the opportunity to feed on crops in farmer's fields, if they get the chance.

Keeping the boys at arms length

The saying 'as mad as a March hare' comes from the fact that brown hares often 'box' each other with their front feet, in early spring. This behaviour was originally thought to be males fighting for access to females, a behaviour seen in many other animals (for example, the red deer). However, in the 1980s it was discovered that most of the 'boxing' matches of hares are actually between males and females. A female will 'box away' the males, if she is not ready to mate. Male hares often chase away other males but they do not normally box each other. Unlike rabbits, hares do not dig burrows. Instead they usually hide in a flattened area of vegetation, or shallow scrape in the earth, called a 'form'. The female also gives birth and keeps her young (called leverets) hidden in a form. A female hare usually has three leverets in each litter and she can have as many as four litters per year. The high rate at which hares (and rabbits) can breed is probably a reason why they are often regarded as a symbol of fertility.

Although hares and rabbits can produce lots of young, lots of them are usually killed and eaten by predators. Hares spend a lot of time in the open, so they are vulnerable to attack by predatory birds such as eagles and buzzards and fast-running predators on the ground. Hares will often lie still on the ground

Golden eagle chasing a hare by Rose Wheal, Melrose Primary School

and rely on their camouflage, until predators get very close. Hares can live to be 12 years old but they rarely survive for longer than five years in the wild.

Hare hunting – for food, 'fun' and farming

Millions of hares (mainly the brown or European hare) are shot for food in Europe every year. The hare is considerably larger than a rabbit and consequently provides a greater quantity of meat. 'Jugged hare' is a common way of cooking hares (with wine and herbs) in Britain.

People also hunt hares with dogs. This is called 'hare coursing'. During hare coursing, fast-running dogs (often lurchers, a cross between collie dogs and greyhounds) are encouraged to chase and catch hares in large open fields.

This method of hunting was banned in Britain at the same time as fox hunting (in 2002 in Scotland and 2004 in England) but it is still a legal sport in some countries.

Hares and rabbits are also shot by farmers to prevent damage to crops. Hares tend to live in lower densities than rabbits and so are usually only shot for this reason if their numbers get unusually high. Low numbers of hares do not usually cause serious damage to crops.

At the moment, large numbers of mountain hares are being killed (culled) in Scotland by people that manage moors for the shooting of red grouse. Mountain hares have been blamed for outbreaks of a disease, called 'louping ill' in red grouse. This disease is transmitted by ticks that live on a variety of animals. Mountain hares are

Brown hare by Stuart Henderson, Belmont House School

a native species and are an important prey item for golden eagles in Scotland, so wildlife conservation organisations have asked for the extent of the culling to be reduced.

Hare coursers convicted by DNA evidence

Several people have been convicted of hare coursing in Scotland with the help of DNA evidence. As illegal hare coursing is often done for 'fun' rather than to provide food, people often dump the bodies of hares that have been killed, rather than take them home.

There have been two cases in Scotland where individual dogs have been identified by collecting samples of dog saliva from dead brown hares that have been dumped. If the police

already suspect that a particular dog owner is involved in hare coursing, they can demand to test their dog. If the DNA 'fingerprint' of the owner's dog matches that of the saliva found on the body of the dead hare, this can provide very strong evidence that the dog was involved in killing the hare.

In 2013 two men from Falkirk were convicted of hare coursing, after the DNA of their dog was found on a dead hare. In 2016, a man from Aberdeen became the first person in Scotland to be jailed for illegally hunting with a dog, based on DNA evidence. He was jailed for four and a half months and his two accomplices from Aberdeen were also convicted. They were seen hunting hares near Kirriemuir in Angus and DNA tests linked their dogs to the body of a dead

Brown hare by Amelie Berry, Earlston High School

hare. The jailed man also had videos and computer records that showed he had been hare coursing at many other locations in Scotland.

In both of these cases, the DNA sampling and analysis was done by staff from the Scottish government's Science and Advice for Agriculture Laboratory (SASA) in Edinburgh.

How many different types of hare are there in the world?

DNA tests are helping to work out how many different types of hare exist in the world today. I am not going to give much detail here because it is not highly relevant to the situation in Scotland and much of this work is at an early stage. However, it is worth pointing out that:

At the moment, there are thought to be 32 different species of hare in the world. Some of them are called jackrabbits but they are more closely related to hares than rabbits.

Many of the hare species have been divided into sub-species. For example, the brown hare (European hare) has in the past been divided into 30 sub-species. But not all of them are now regarded as 'true' sub-species by scientists, because many of them are very similar.

Different species often cannot breed with each other. But many species (and sub-species) of hare can breed with each other, even though they may not normally do so in their natural environment.

The brown hare is a different species from the mountain hare but

Brown hare by Catherine Mole, James Gillespie's High School

Brown hare on the island of Coll   © Pete Minting

OF THE 32 SPECIES OF HARE WORLDWIDE, NINE ARE AT RISK OF EXTINCTION. SEVERAL SUB-SPECIES ARE ALSO AT RISK OF EXTINCTION AND SOME MAY HAVE RECENTLY GONE EXTINCT (FOR INSTANCE THE MAJORCAN HARE, A SUB-SPECIES OF THE BROWN HARE).

they can interbreed or 'hybridise' with each other. This has been recorded in Denmark, where both species exist but hybridisation between brown hares and mountain hares has not been recorded in the wild in Britain.

Of the 32 species of hare worldwide, nine are at risk of extinction (classed as near threatened, vulnerable or endangered). Several sub-species are also at risk of extinction and some may have recently gone extinct (for instance the Majorcan hare, a sub-species of the brown hare). However, the two hares found in Britain are considered as 'least concern' in terms of extinction risk.

Hares and rabbits are quite closely related to rodents but belong to a separate group or 'order' of mammals called 'lagomorphs'. Lagomorphs and rodents are both herbivorous and usually have large front teeth (incisors), specially-adapted for feeding on tough vegetation.

Factsheets about many British mammals, including the brown hare, mountain hare and European rabbit can be downloaded from the Mammal Society's website: **www.mammal.org.uk/discover-mammals**

07
Water vole

VOLES BELONG TO A LARGE GROUP OF MAMMALS CALLED 'RODENTS' THAT ALSO INCLUDES MICE, RATS, GERBILS, HAMSTERS, SQUIRRELS AND BEAVERS. WATER VOLES LOOK A BIT LIKE HAMSTERS BUT THEY ARE SLIGHTLY BIGGER THAN A GOLDEN HAMSTER. MOST WATER VOLES ARE BROWN BUT IN SCOTLAND, MANY ARE BLACK.

The water vole has a shorter tail than a rat or mouse

© Laurie Campbell

Water voles are usually brown (above left) but in Scotland, many of them are black (above right) © Laurie Campbell

IF YOU SEE A HAMSTER-LIKE ANIMAL SWIMMING ACROSS A RIVER, OR
NIBBLING AT PLANTS BY THE SIDE OF A DITCH, IT MIGHT BE A WATER VOLE.

WATER VOLES

by Poppy Young, Coldingham Primary School

People often call me a water rat, even though I'm a water vole. I have a chubby face, short fuzzy ears and deep brown fur. Rats have a smaller nose and no hair on their ears, tails and paws. In the wild, water voles like me live (on average) for about two and a half years.

In Britain, water voles live in burrows in banks (not the ones you get money from); by rivers, ditches, ponds and streams. Our diet is mainly grass or plants near the water. We are experts at swimming and diving. We scent our homes by marking them with secretions from our bodies.

We start mating by the end of March, right through until autumn. A female water vole's pregnancy usually lasts for twenty one days and she can have up to eight babies. Water vole numbers have dropped by a lot, so please help to save us!

When compared to most other voles, such as the field vole, the water vole is much bigger and is often mistaken for a rat. The character 'Ratty' in the book *Wind in the Willows* is not a rat – he is a water vole. In Britain (including Scotland), water voles are usually found living next to small rivers or ditches.

If you see a hamster-like animal swimming across a river, or nibbling at plants by the side of a ditch, it might be a water vole. Rats (such as the brown rat) are also commonly seen alongside rivers but they have long, largely hairless tails, which you will probably be able to see. Water voles have a fairly short tail, which is not as short as a hamster's tail but shorter than the tail of a rat or mouse.

No defence against the mink

Water voles have declined dramatically in Britain (including Scotland). One of the main causes is thought to be the introduction of American mink but other factors, such as habitat destruction, are

Water vole by Jenny O'Gorman, George Watson's College

also to blame. The American mink is a predator that belongs to the same family of mammals as stoats, otters, badgers and pine martens but as its name suggests, it is not native to Britain.

Mink fur is often used to make fur coats. When demand for fur coats dropped in many countries (including Britain) in the 1970s, many mink farms closed and large numbers of mink were released into the wild. At the time of writing this book, the number of mink farms was increasing again worldwide, largely due to demand for fur by people in Russia and China.

It has been illegal to farm animals for their fur in Scotland since 2002, so large releases of mink are unlikely to happen again here but attempts to eradicate them have failed and they are still fairly widespread in Scotland. The government's wildlife agency Scottish Natural Heritage (SNH) now argues that the best approach is to control their numbers and limit the damage that they cause.

Mink do very well in Britain because the climate and landscape is similar to where they come from and there are many animals that they can prey upon, including water voles. Mink are small enough to enter the burrows of water

The American mink is very good at hunting water voles
© Laurie Campbell

voles, so they can kill and eat them.

In some places in Britain water voles are managing to cling on in low numbers, despite the presence of mink. In Scotland, efforts have been made by the Ayrshire Rivers Trust to save a water vole population in Troon, by improving their habitat, catching mink and boosting water vole numbers by captive-breeding. There are several other similar projects taking place across Britain.

The removal of mink would benefit many other native species in Britain. But trapping and killing them is controversial. Like the sika deer (mentioned in the red deer chapter), it is not the mink's fault that it has been introduced by people to other countries.

Ratty's rescue ridiculed by BBC

In 2015, the BBC (in an article on the BBC's news website) quoted a farmer who claimed that water voles would just "move from the riverbanks to the fields" if machinery was used to deepen (dredge) a river on his land. The headline of the article also appeared to

suggest that it was ridiculous to spend a lot of money on rescuing water voles.

Most water voles create their burrows on steep, grassy river banks. These burrows normally provide the water vole with a safe place to hide from predators. Sometimes the burrow entrances are under water (a bit like the entrances to beaver lodges, as described in the chapter on beavers). In Britain, water voles feed mainly on plants that are found in or next to rivers.

Dredging machines are often used to deepen rivers (dredging) and diggers are often used to straighten them ('canalisation'). But many animals (such as salmon, rare mussels, mayflies, kingfishers and otters) depend on the existence of natural river beds and riverbanks, which are often damaged or destroyed by dredging and canalisation. Dredging often results in removal of the plants that water voles feed on and canalisation destroys their burrows.

Dredging often backfires by moving the problem further downstream. Sometimes it does not work at all.

Water vole by Jodie Sharp, Kirkintilloch High School

THE WATER VOLES THAT ARE NATIVE TO SCOTLAND APPEAR (FROM DNA EVIDENCE) TO HAVE COME FROM THE PART OF EUROPE WHICH IS NOW SPAIN AND PORTUGAL.

More information about water voles can be found here: www.nature.scot/plants-animals-and-fungi/mammals/land-mammals/water-voles

Scottish water voles have Spanish roots

Many animals (including people) on either side of the border between Scotland and England frequently interbreed with each other, so in genetic terms, they could be regarded as belonging to the same populations. But the same is not true of water voles. The water voles that are native to Scotland appear (from DNA evidence) to have come from the part of Europe which is now Spain and Portugal. The water voles that are found today in England (and Wales) are more similar to water voles from north-eastern Europe, including those that are found today in Finland.

How did water voles get to Scotland from Spain? After the end of the last ice age, about 15,000 years ago many animals and plants moved north and recolonised northern Europe. During the peaks of the ice ages, water voles (and many other European species) had survived in places that remained free of ice in southern Europe.

When the ice melted, there was a period of time when European wildlife had the chance to recolonise Britain over

For example, if it is done near to the mouth of a river (estuary), mud and sand often refills the deepened channels after a few high tides. It is much better to prevent flooding by slowing the rate at which rain water enters rivers, for instance by reforesting upland areas, or the use of 'sustainable drainage systems' (SuDS) in as many places as possible.

Article about money spent on water voles: www.bbc.co.uk/news/uk-england-somerset-32127454

Let Ratty live in peace by the riverbank

Since 1998, water voles have been protected by an addition to the Wildlife and Countryside Act (1981) which means that it is illegal to disturb them or damage the places (such as their burrows) where they are resting. But if people do not know that water voles are present, they may not be protected, so if you see a water vole in Scotland, try and record it on an online recording scheme for wildlife, or report it to Scottish Natural Heritage (SNH).

ICED PAWS

by Cona Maitland, St Joseph's Academy, Kilmarnock

The little water vole was stranded deep underground. He was snowed in! Every elaborately twisted tunnel towards the surface was filled with dreaded snow. He couldn't get out and there was nothing to eat, apart from a few twigs and blades of grass.

The amount of effort he put in was astonishing, but there was nothing he could do. He just couldn't get out. He tried digging a hole but that did nothing. He felt downright useless and his spirits began to waver.

But then, out of nowhere, a warm feeling of heat hit his small body. A ray of hope in the form of light started to melt its way through. He scurried out of his burrow to see the start of spring. The beautiful park came back to life. The once bare trees had beautiful pink blossoms and the buried pathway now stood clear. With winter gone, he could do anything!

land, before Britain was separated from mainland Europe by the expansion of the English Channel. DNA evidence suggests that the water voles in Scotland came from an ice-free 'refuge' in south-western Europe (probably somewhere in Spain or Portugal), whereas the water voles in England, Wales and Finland came from a different refuge in south-eastern Europe.

Who cares where water voles came from?

You may be wondering why this matters. But it is useful to know which species are native to Britain and how different populations are related to each other. For example, people who are captive-breeding and reintroducing water voles sometimes have to get their 'breeding stock' from somewhere else, if the water vole has become extinct in their local area. It is often best to source stock from a similar population. At the moment, the water voles in Scotland are not

considered a separate sub-species from those in England and Wales but they are slightly different.

It is also useful to know what is likely to happen if the climate in a cold area starts to warm up, as a result of global warming. On an island like Britain, the movements of many species will be limited by the sea but in other parts of the world, they may be able to move north or south towards the poles, as the planet warms up. This is likely to have impacts on people, as well as wildlife.

Small rodents are ideal for studying the history of climate change and wildlife, because they often exist in large numbers and their hard teeth (adapted for eating tough vegetation) survive for a long time if they are buried in the ground. Just one bone (or tooth) can be enough to identify and confirm the presence of an animal and the past existence of a climate which was suitable for its survival.

08
Golden eagle

THE GOLDEN EAGLE CAN SOAR EFFORTLESSLY TO GREAT HEIGHTS, BY MAKING USE OF RISING AIR CURRENTS. IF IT SPOTS ITS PREY ON THE GROUND, IT CAN REACH INCREDIBLE SPEEDS AS IT PLUMMETS BACK TOWARDS THE EARTH, LEAVING ITS TARGET (SUCH AS A HARE OR RABBIT) JUST A FEW SECONDS TO REACT AND DASH FOR COVER.

Golden eagle

© Laurie Campbell

Golden eagle, soaring with its wings outstretched © Laurie Campbell

IN 2015, THERE WERE 508 PAIRS OF
GOLDEN EAGLES IN BRITAIN
(ALL OF THEM IN SCOTLAND).

It is hard to find words which can
adequately describe the beauty of a
golden eagle. Luckily, we have been
helped out by a talented young artist
(Amy O'Keefe), who has somehow
managed to capture the spirit of this
amazing bird on paper, using nothing
more than a pencil (front cover, and
right). And Laurie Campbell, who has
been photographing Scottish wildlife for
decades, has provided us with some
excellent photographs.

Most widely-distributed eagle in the world

The golden eagle is the most widely-
distributed species of eagle in the
world. It is native to most of the land in
the northern hemisphere but is found
mainly between the Tropic of Cancer
(23 degrees north of the Equator) and
the Arctic Circle (about 66 degrees
north). It has disappeared from many
places where it used to exist, often as a
result of habitat loss. Worldwide, there
are many sub-species of golden eagle but
they all look fairly similar.

Golden eagles maintain very large
territories and although they have a wide
distribution globally, they tend to exist at
low population densities when compared
to most other birds. In 2015, there were
508 pairs of golden eagles in Britain (all
of them in Scotland).

Portrait of a golden eagle by Amy O'Keefe, Greenfaulds High School

Second fastest animal on the planet?

The golden eagle is a close contender for the title of 'fastest animal on the planet' (apart from humans in powered vehicles). The peregrine falcon is slightly faster but both of these birds can exceed 320 kilometres per hour (200 mph) when diving or 'stooping' in flight, to catch prey.

In Scotland, the diet of the golden eagle largely consists of mountain hares, rabbits, grouse (including ptarmigan), young deer, seabirds and dead animals (carrion). Another amazing feature of the golden eagle, other than its phenomenal speed, is its eyesight. The golden eagle (like many other birds that soar at a great height to spot food) has densely-packed cells in a special area within the back of its eyes, which means it can see prey clearly up to two kilometres away.

The golden eagle is adapted to hunting in open areas and rarely hunts in woodlands. It is a large eagle, with most males in Scotland having a wingspan of just under two metres and females just over two metres. Golden eagles have huge talons and are capable of killing small deer.

TODAY, DESPITE THE EXISTENCE OF SEVERAL LAWS WHICH SHOULD PROTECT THEM, MANY BIRDS OF PREY (INCLUDING GOLDEN EAGLES) ARE STILL BEING ILLEGALLY KILLED IN BRITAIN.

GOLDEN EAGLE

by Donald 'Archie' Campbell, Ardnamurchan High School

The sight of a golden eagle
Brief but beautiful
Like a gust of wind

The eagle in the sky
calm and peaceful
An image of serenity

The golden eagle soars across the sky
I wonder what it's like
To be free...

Challenging bird for a falconer

Golden eagles are popular birds with falconers (people who use birds of prey for hunting or display purposes). However, it is not a suitable bird for inexperienced falconers as it is very large and has the potential to inflict serious injury, if not trained or handled properly.

I have included more details on the history of falconry in the chapter on goshawks. However, it is worth pointing out that young golden eagles are occasionally taken from nests in the wild for use in falconry. In Britain, this is illegal without a licence and today this rarely occurs in Britain. In other parts of

Golden eagle with chick in nest (photography licensed by SNH)   © Laurie Campbell

Golden eagle   © Laurie Campbell

the world (such as Russia and China) eaglets are often taken for use in falconry.

Ongoing persecution

I have included more detail about the history of wildlife persecution in Britain in the chapters on goshawks and badgers, so I will not repeat that information here. However, it is worth pointing out that the golden eagle has been treated in a similar way to the goshawk and it was very rare in Britain by the early 1900s, largely as a result of persecution by gamekeepers.

Today, despite the existence of several laws which should protect them, many birds of prey (including golden eagles) are still being illegally killed in Britain. They are often persecuted by gamekeepers in areas where gamebirds

(such as pheasants and grouse) are being reared for shooting. They can also become accidental victims of poisons and traps put out by farmers to try and kill other animals, such as rats and foxes.

Some trapping and poisoning methods are legal. If legal methods are used, birds of prey are unlikely to be killed. For example, metal spring traps can be used inside mesh tunnels on the ground but it has been illegal (since 1904) to put them on top of a post (a 'pole trap'), because this kills birds.

Birds of prey (and other animals) are often killed when gamekeepers (illegally) put poisoned meat out in the open. Although golden eagles can catch live prey, they will also feed on dead animals and with their amazing eyesight, they can spot dead animals from miles away. At least 27 golden eagles have been killed

Golden eagle (with satellite tag) illegally killed in Scotland in 2012   © RSPB Scotland

by poisoning in Scotland since 1994. Many more will have been poisoned (or killed by other methods) and their bodies removed, to hide the evidence.

In May 2017, the Scottish government published a report which concluded that, nearly a third (41/131) of golden eagles fitted with tracking devices in Scotland (from 2004 to 2016) disappeared in mysterious circumstances and were probably killed by people. The results suggest that much of the persecution occurred in the central and eastern Highlands (roughly, inside a triangle linking Perth, Inverness and Aberdeen). But the problem is widespread and golden eagles have recently been poisoned in many parts of Scotland, including the Borders (where they are very rare) and in Argyllshire (for

example, at Bridge of Orchy in 2009). The full report is available here: **www.snh.org.uk/pdfs/publications/ commissioned_reports/982.pdf** It is taking a long time for poisons (such as carbofuran) which are often used to kill birds of prey, to be effectively banned in Britain. Several of the most powerful people in Britain (who strongly influence law-making) participate in shooting events, or own grouse moors. In 2012, it was reported that Richard Benyon had refused to make possession of carbofuran an offence in England and Wales (see article by The Independent here: **https://tinyurl.com/9gvencc**).

Birds of prey are also illegally shot and it is easy for people to get away with this in remote places. The Royal Society for the Protection of Birds (RSPB) has

THE PERSECUTION OF GOLDEN EAGLES MEANS THAT THE BRITISH
POPULATION IS WELL BELOW 'CARRYING CAPACITY'. IN OTHER WORDS,
IF PERSECUTION STOPPED, IT IS LIKELY THAT AT LEAST ANOTHER 100
PAIRS OF GOLDEN EAGLES COULD EXIST IN NORTHERN BRITAIN, BASED
ON THE AVAILABILITY OF PREY AND SUITABLE HABITAT.

occasionally recorded the illegal shooting of wild birds of prey, including a video of a man shooting a hen harrier on Cabrach Estate in Morayshire in 2013. A judge ruled that the RSPB had conducted 'covert surveillance' without permission on the land where the shooting took place, so their evidence was rejected. The RSPB claimed that their evidence had been collected during standard monitoring of hen harrier populations.

In Scotland, the public are entitled (by the Land Reform Act, 2003) to access the majority of open land, including the land where hen harriers and golden eagles are most likely to be seen (moors and mountains). Similar rules exist in England and Wales under the Countryside and Rights of Way Act (CROW Act, 2000). It is legal to take photographs or videos on land where there is public access. If you see or record any evidence of a wildlife crime, report it immediately to the police.

In Scotland, a new law has been introduced (as part of the Wildlife and Natural Environment Act, 2011) which means that landowners can be held responsible for illegal activities (including wildlife crimes) which occur on their land, even if there is no evidence that the owner is directly involved. This 'vicarious liability' rule may help to reduce the persecution of wildlife, including birds of prey.

The persecution of golden eagles means that the British population is well below 'carrying capacity'. In other words, if persecution stopped, it is likely that at least another 100 pairs of golden eagles could exist in northern Britain, based on the availability of prey and suitable habitat.

Population on Outer Hebrides isolated from mainland

In 2015, DNA evidence was published that suggests golden eagles on the Outer Hebrides are fairly isolated from those on mainland Scotland (or the Inner Hebrides). Before then, it was thought that golden eagles from these islands and the mainland regularly interbred with each other.

This DNA evidence was collected largely from feathers. Birds regularly shed and re-grow their feathers, so it is possible to collect them for DNA testing without handling or harming the birds. It is easiest to extract 'high quality' DNA from large feathers because they usually contain tiny, natural blood clots in the shaft, near to where the feather joins the bird's body.

Once DNA 'fingerprints' have been created for individual birds (by sampling several parts of the genome), it is possible to compare these against the DNA profiles of newly-collected feathers, to see if there is a match. In this way, scientists can find out when 'new' birds arrive, where 'known' birds move to and

A white-tailed sea eagle on Mull in western Scotland

© Laurie Campbell

UNTIL RECENTLY, IF YOU SAW A BIRD WITH AN ENORMOUS TWO-METRE WINGSPAN, SOARING HIGH ABOVE YOU IN SCOTLAND, YOU COULD BE FAIRLY SURE THAT IT WOULD BE A GOLDEN EAGLE. BUT THE REINTRODUCTION OF THE WHITE-TAILED SEA EAGLE MEANS THAT SCOTLAND NOW HAS TWO 'NATIVE' SPECIES OF EAGLE.

work out how long they live in the wild.

The evidence from the study in 2015 suggests that the 'founders' of the golden eagle population on the Outer Hebrides originally came from the mainland, but it also shows that today, gene flow is limited and mainly occurs in the opposite direction. In other words, a few golden eagles from the Outer Hebrides are moving to the mainland to breed but hardly any golden eagles are leaving the Scottish mainland to breed on the Outer Hebrides.

This could be because (at the moment) there is a denser population of golden eagles on the Outer Hebrides than on the mainland, where they are still suffering from persecution. A similar pattern has been seen in California. Sometimes islands can act as a refuge for species that are suffering elsewhere. In many birds, if the population grows and there is an increase in competition for food or territories, young birds are more likely to travel further away to find a new territory.

But compared to many other birds, golden eagles are not keen to cross large expanses of sea. The minimum distance between the Scottish mainland and the Outer Hebrides is 40 km. This does not sound very far for a bird to travel but the DNA evidence suggests that golden eagles from the mainland rarely mix with those on the Outer Hebrides. In some parts of the world, golden eagles

are much more migratory but here, they prefer to stay fairly close to their original or 'natal' nest.

Long-lost cousin returns to Scotland

Until recently, if you saw a bird with an enormous two-metre wingspan, soaring high above you in Scotland, you could be fairly sure that it would be a golden eagle. But the reintroduction of the white-tailed sea eagle means that Scotland now has two 'native' species of eagle.

White-tailed sea eagles became extinct in Scotland in 1916 and there is no-one alive today who can remember seeing them here in the early 1900s. In 1975, reintroduction projects (using birds sourced from Norway) began and they have now become re-established. According to the Scottish Code for Conservation Translocations (2014), no species which has gone extinct in Scotland is 'technically' native after it has been reintroduced but the white-tailed sea eagle is undoubtedly a native species.

Compared to the golden eagle, a white-tailed sea eagle has a shorter tail, longer neck and broader, longer wings. They also behave a bit differently. Unlike the golden eagle, which usually hunts over land, the white-tailed sea eagle can also catch fish in water (a bit like the osprey) and often steals fish from other predators, such as otters.

An abandoned golden eagle nest (photography licensed by SNH) © Laurie Campbell

Manx shearwater eggs from a legal collection © CSG CIC Glasgow Museums Collection

The white-tailed sea eagle hunts many of the same animals as the golden eagle (such as hares and rabbits) but unlike the golden eagle, it regularly stalks other predators along the seashore and tries to steal their catch.

One of the easiest places to see this bird (and the golden eagle) is on the island of Mull. Mull is now an excellent place for wildlife-watching and in recent years, the island's economy has been boosted by an increase in wildlife tourism.

DNA evidence helps to jail illegal egg collector

It is illegal to collect or destroy the eggs of nearly all wild birds in Britain (including Scotland), under the Protection of Birds Act (1954). Occasionally the government will issue a licence to allow egg collection (for scientific research, for example) but egg collection is usually illegal.

In 2012, a man from London was jailed for six months and banned from entering Scotland (during the bird breeding season) for 10 years, after he was caught illegally collecting eggs. He had been arrested on the Scottish island of Rum and was found to be carrying boxes of wild bird eggs, including eggs from a rare bird called the Manx shearwater.

Egg collectors remove the contents of eggs using an 'egg-blowing kit'. The kit owned by this egg collector was confiscated by the police and subjected to DNA tests. It tested positive for Manx shearwater DNA, which helped to prove

A tray of eggs legally collected before 1954 © CSG CIC Glasgow Museums Collection

that he had processed the eggs stolen from Rum.

When his home in London was searched, police found 700 more eggs in his collection, from a variety of wild birds. The DNA testing in this case was done by the Scottish government's wildlife forensic laboratory at Science and Advice for Scottish Agriculture (SASA) in Edinburgh.

Any wild bird in Britain could benefit from the use of DNA technology, to help catch illegal egg collectors. Egg collecting is still legal in some other countries, so the police often need plenty of evidence if a collector is to be convicted, such as evidence that he (or she) has visited sites in Britain.

Egg collectors often target the nests of birds of prey, including golden eagles. Collectors often take all of the eggs from a nest, and even if they do not take the entire clutch, the adult birds will often abandon the nest as a result of the disturbance.

Sometimes egg collectors smash up their collections when the police arrive. In such cases, DNA tests can be done to confirm the species identity of the eggs. It is not illegal to possess eggs from farmed or pet birds (such as domestic chickens, or pet canaries), so once they have been smashed, it can be difficult to prove (without DNA tests and other evidence) that a crime has been committed.

09
Goshawk

THE GOSHAWK IS A STUNNING AND FIERCE-LOOKING BIRD OF PREY. IT HAS BRIGHT YELLOW OR ORANGE EYES AND SIMILARLY BRIGHT YELLOW LEGS. THE FIRST GOSHAWK I SAW LANDED ON THE GROUND RIGHT IN FRONT OF ME, WITH A WOOD PIGEON IN ITS TALONS. IT RIPPED AT THE PIGEON WITH ITS HOOKED BEAK AND HUNDREDS OF THE PIGEON'S WHITE, DOWNY FEATHERS DRIFTED ACROSS THE GRASS, LIKE SNOW. I KNEW THIS COULD NOT BE A SPARROWHAWK BECAUSE I HAD SEEN ONE OF THEM EARLIER, CHASING A GOLDFINCH. THIS WAS A MUCH BIGGER BIRD.

Goshawk © Laurie Campbell

82

BY THE EARLY 1900S, GOSHAWKS HAD BEEN ON THE 'HIT LIST' OF BRITISH LANDOWNERS FOR CENTURIES. AT THIS TIME, NO MORE THAN 4% OF BRITAIN WAS COVERED BY TREES, WHICH MEANT THAT IT WAS FAIRLY EASY TO FIND AND DESTROY GOSHAWK NESTS.

I froze to the spot and luckily the goshawk did not appear to see me but after a few minutes it took off, carrying what was left of the unfortunate pigeon. That was more than 20 years ago and since then I have only seen one other goshawk, which flew across the road in front of my car, in a forest near Newton Stewart in Dumfries and Galloway.

The native species of goshawk in Britain is called the 'northern goshawk'. Although it is native to Britain (including Scotland) and is widely-distributed across much of northern Europe, northern Asia and North America, the goshawk is rare in Britain and it has probably been rare here since the late 1700s. It was almost extinct in Britain from 1900 until 1965.

The ability of the goshawk to hunt relatively large birds and animals, including grouse, pheasants, chickens and rabbits has put it in conflict with farmers and gamekeepers, who often see it as a threat to their livelihoods. Laws passed in the 1500s (which were not scrapped until the late 1800s) encouraged the killing of any wildlife that was seen as a threat to farming or hunting.

By the early 1900s, goshawks had been on the 'hit list' of British landowners for centuries. At this time, no more than 4% of Britain was covered by trees, which meant that it was fairly easy to find and destroy goshawk nests.

Goshawks usually nest in woodlands in tall trees (at least 10m off the ground). Although it has been illegal to collect the eggs of wild birds in Britain since 1954, some egg collectors still raid goshawk nests. The goshawk is also popular with falconers (people who train and use birds of prey for hunting), partly because it can hunt in a variety of habitats, unlike many other birds of prey.

In mediaeval times, the goshawk was regarded as a suitable hunting bird for someone fairly important. The Bayeux tapestry, which records the Norman invasion of England in the 11th century, shows several noblemen carrying large hawks, which could be goshawks. The title of the novel *A Kestrel for a Knave* (by Barry Hines) is from a list in a 15th century manuscript, which gives advice on hunting, including hunting with hawks:

*"An eagle for an emperor, a gyrfalcon for a king; a peregrine for a prince, a saker for a knight, a merlin for a lady; a **goshawk for a yeoman**, a sparrowhawk for a priest, a musket for a holy water clerk, a kestrel for a knave."* A yeoman would have owned some land and would probably have been associated with the royal family at that time.

Nearly a thousand years after the Norman invasion, goshawks are still highly prized by falconers. Young goshawks are still occasionally taken from nests in the wild for use in falconry

Goshawk by Terri Simpson, Arbroath Academy

BY THE EARLY 1900S, GOSHAWKS HAD BEEN ON THE 'HIT LIST' OF BRITISH LANDOWNERS FOR CENTURIES. AT THIS TIME, NO MORE THAN 4% OF BRITAIN WAS COVERED BY TREES, WHICH MEANT THAT IT WAS FAIRLY EASY TO FIND AND DESTROY GOSHAWK NESTS.

(but this is now illegal, unless you have a licence). Goshawks are considered so valuable that people still go to great lengths to capture or keep them, sometimes breaking the law in the process.

In the 1960s, the number of people who were interested in protecting wildlife grew rapidly. Several attempts to reintroduce the goshawk to Britain took place in the 1960s and 1970s. Progress was slow and this appeared to be a result of ongoing persecution, largely by landowners and gamekeepers who still regarded goshawks as a threat to gamebirds (such as pheasants and partridges)

which are commercially-reared and then released for people to shoot.

Goshawks are now doing reasonably well in areas of Britain with large forests (such as Dumfries and Galloway in Scotland and Northumberland in northern England) but are still vulnerable to persecution, illegal collecting and disturbance. Commercial conifer forests can provide suitable habitat but goshawks often abandon their nests, if disturbed by people or logging machines.

Goshawks are usually regarded as a 'resident' species because they rarely migrate over long distances. They will sometimes disperse into new areas if they cannot find enough food but they generally stay within 100 km of the nest where they hatched. Although goshawks from mainland Europe occasionally cross the North Sea into Britain, their tendency to stay close to home may be another reason why their recovery rate has been quite slow.

DNA technology and the northern goshawk

There are several ways in which DNA technology has been used to study or protect goshawks.

DNA evidence shows that the northern goshawk is most closely-related to other birds of prey called harriers, such as the hen harrier and marsh harrier, not

Goshawks can hunt in woodland as well as open areas

© Laurie Campbell

those that have the most similar names (such as the pale and dark chanting goshawks). Before DNA technology was invented, scientists usually put living things into groups based on their similarities in terms of appearance and behaviour. We now know (from DNA evidence) that many of these groupings were wrong and many species have now been re-named, or re-classified. Often these mistakes happened because different species tend to evolve similar features to each other, if they do similar things and live in a similar environment. Many animals have evolved striped patterns, for example, which provide useful camouflage but many of these animals are not closely related.

Goshawk by Gregor Sharkey, Lockerbie Academy

Unique feather patterns

In 2016, scientists in Scotland (from Aberdeen University and Natural Research Ltd) published a study which proved that goshawks have individual patterns on their feathers, like human fingerprints. Bird experts had suspected for years that many birds, including goshawks, had individual differences in the markings of their feathers. To work out if it was really possible to recognise individual goshawks from their feathers, the scientists DNA-tested a large sample of feathers from different goshawks and gave them to the bird experts to identify. The feathers tested were 'inner primary' feathers, which are used in flight but are regularly shed and re-grown.

The results showed that it was possible to identify adult goshawks from the 'barred' patterns on their inner primaries. This means that it is not always necessary to do expensive DNA tests to identify individual goshawks. Instead, people can just pick up feathers from places where goshawks have been roosting or perching, to see if any new individuals have visited the

area, or taken over nests that used to be occupied by other goshawks. Many birds of prey, including goshawks, will visit or take over the nests or territories of other individuals but this can be hard to detect. The addition of feather identification to the toolbox of methods for goshawk monitoring will improve our understanding of this species (including their breeding behaviour, population estimates and how far they move), without costing any more money.

Goshawk identity fraud

DNA evidence has also been used to work out whether people have been lying about the origin of captive goshawks in their possession. In 2009 the owner of a pair of goshawks in England was convicted of possessing a wild goshawk. He had legally obtained the pair from Hungary in 1987 and properly registered them at that time but when the female died, he tried to replace it with a new wild goshawk. He claimed that tags on the old female had fallen off or stopped working but when he asked a vet to visit

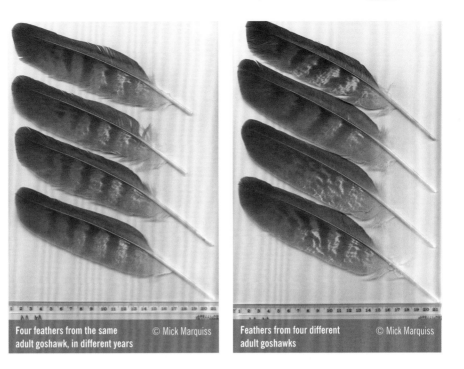

Four feathers from the same
adult goshawk, in different years
© Mick Marquiss

Feathers from four different
adult goshawks
© Mick Marquiss

and re-tag it, the vet became suspicious that it was a new and younger bird.

The goshawk keeper in this case had sold several offspring from the original pair to other falconers. DNA tests done on these birds showed that they could not be the offspring of the female that was now in his possession. At some point, he must have replaced the original female goshawk with a another one that was probably illegally taken from the wild (possibly in Britain), because he was unable to explain where it had come from. All legally-owned, captive goshawks in Britain (including those bred in captivity) are tagged and on a list of registered birds.

More details of this case were published in volume 60 of 'Legal Eagle', a newsletter by the Royal Society for the Protection of Birds (RSPB) which can be downloaded from:
ww2.rspb.org.uk/our-work/our-positions-and-campaigns/positions/wildbirdslaw/legalpublications.aspx

If falconers know that DNA technology can be used to check on the identity of their birds, they may be less likely to try and cheat, or buy birds of unknown origin. Another way in which DNA technology can be used to help protect birds, including goshawks, is to identify the species of illegally-collected bird's eggs. There are more details on this in the chapter on golden eagles.

ALL LEGALLY-OWNED, CAPTIVE GOSHAWKS IN BRITAIN (INCLUDING THOSE BRED IN CAPTIVITY) ARE TAGGED AND ON A LIST OF REGISTERED BIRDS.

10
Capercaillie

THE NAME CAPERCAILLIE DERIVES FROM THE SCOTTISH GAELIC *CAPULL COILLE* WHICH MEANS 'HORSE OF THE WOODS'. WHEN DISPLAYING TO FEMALES OR DEFENDING HIS TERRITORY, THE MALE CAPERCAILLIE GIVES A LOUD 'CLIP-CLOPPING' CALL, WHICH FROM A DISTANCE, CAN SOUND LIKE A HORSE WALKING.

Male capercaillie with raised tail, during breeding display   © Laurie Campbell

The female capercaillie prefers to stay out of danger   © Laurie Campbell

The capercaillie is the largest species of grouse in the world. Adult male capercaillies usually weigh about 4 kg (the same as a typical Christmas turkey in Britain). Males and females look very different. The male is predominantly black, with a few white markings and a distinctive red 'eyebrow'. The female is smaller than the male and is camouflaged by a combination of rusty brown, grey, white and black feathers.

The species of capercaillie that is native to Britain is called the western capercaillie. In Britain, the capercaillie is now only found in Scotland but it may have lived in other parts of Britain, hundreds of years ago. There are several other isolated populations of capercaillie in western Europe (for instance in northern Spain and Germany). The western capercaillie is native to many parts of Europe and Asia and usually inhabits mature, natural conifer forests with a cool climate. The almost-continuous 'taiga' or 'boreal forest' across northern Europe and Asia is a very important habitat for the capercaillie and today, this is where the largest populations are found.

Historical evidence suggests that the capercaillie probably became extinct in Scotland between 1770 and 1785. From the early 1800s, several attempts were made to reintroduce them, using capercaillies from Sweden, with the first successful reintroduction taking place in 1837. Since then, they have managed to survive but are again on the brink of local extinction; in 2018, less than 2,000 adult capercaillie may exist in Scotland. Worldwide, they are not endangered and are considered a species of 'least concern' by the International Union for the Conservation of Nature (IUCN).

Capercaillie by Esmé Tilling, Ardnamurchan High School

Although the capercaillie is not regarded as an endangered species at an international level, it is regarded as an important part of Scotland's natural heritage. In Britain (including Scotland) it is illegal to hunt the capercaillie, as it is protected by the Wildlife and Countryside Act (1981). It has never been a popular bird for people to eat, partly because it has a strong flavour (possibly as a result of its diet, which includes bitter-tasting pine needles).

There are three other species of grouse that are native to the UK, the red grouse, the black grouse and the ptarmigan. The capercaillie is much larger than any of these three species but a male black grouse might be mistaken for a male capercaillie, as they are similar in terms of shape and colour.

Battle for survival on at least four fronts

1. **Habitat loss**: this is probably the greatest problem faced by the capercaillie in Scotland. Large areas of mature forest are needed to support a capercaillie population. The forest needs to be well-lit, to allow the growth of bilberry or cowberry plants on the ground. Commercial plantations of Sitka and Norway spruce do not provide suitable habitat, because they are usually too dark inside and the trees are planted too close together. The 'Caledonian' pine forest which occurs naturally in Scotland is ideal but this is a rare habitat. Several organisations are now trying to protect and create more Caledonian pine forest, so this situation might improve. Commercial plantations of Scots pine can also provide suitable habitat, if managed appropriately for capercaillie.

2. **Fencing**: flying birds often crash into things that they cannot see, such as transparent windows, or thin wires. The capercaillie frequently dies as a result of flying into wire fences. Wire fences are often put up to protect young trees in commercial forestry plantations from grazing by deer. Many fields alongside woodlands are also fenced, to prevent farm animals escaping.

3. **Predation**: the capercaillie nests on the ground and its eggs and chicks are vulnerable to a variety of predators, especially foxes and crows but also pine martens. The pine marten, which is also a protected species in Britain, has recently made a good recovery from persecution by people (see separate chapter on the pine marten). There is some evidence of pine martens raiding capercaillie

Male capercaillie in Caledonian pine forest

© Laurie Campbell

Female capercaillie   © Laurie Campbell

IF YOU ARE MOVING ALONG A WOODLAND TRACK AND YOU HAPPEN TO CROSS THE TERRITORY OF A MALE CAPERCAILLIE IN THE BREEDING SEASON, YOU MAY FIND YOURSELF BEING CHASED, OR EVEN PECKED.

nests in Scotland but they are both native species, which co-existed here for thousands of years before humans had a big impact. Humans also drove other native predators, such as the wolf, to extinction. The wolf would have had a limiting effect on medium-sized predators, such as the fox.

4. **Disturbance**: if you are moving along a woodland track and you happen to cross the territory of a male capercaillie in the breeding season, you may find yourself being chased, or even pecked. There are numerous videos on the internet showing male capercaillie trying to scare people away from their breeding territories. Disturbance could be a serious problem for the capercaillie in Scotland; the female capercaillie is only able to mate for very short periods of time, so if the males are constantly disturbed by people, this could result in the birds failing to breed.

Buds, berries, beetles and needles...

The capercaillie can eat a variety of plants but often targets the buds and young leaves of plants on the forest floor, plus berries when they are in season. Bilberries (often known as 'blaeberries' in Scotland) are an important part of the capercaillie's diet.

Although adult capercaillies mainly eat plants, capercaillie chicks also prey on insects, such as beetles, which provide them with enough protein for growth. A female capercaillie lays (on average) eight eggs in a clutch but few of them survive to adulthood. In winter, adults can survive largely on pine needles, if there is snow on the ground and they cannot reach plants hidden under the snow.

Capercaillie to benefit from new DNA project in Scotland

It can be very difficult to count capercaillies, partly because they live in woodland. Other types of bird (such as geese) that live in more open habitats can be a lot easier to count by eye, using a pair of binoculars. It is important to know how many capercaillie are left in Scotland and which areas of habitat they are using, in order to plan efforts to protect them.

In 2014, scientists from mainland Europe published some interesting DNA evidence collected from a capercaillie population in the Bohemian Forest (in Germany and the Czech Republic). In this study, the scientists managed to identify individual capercaillies

The blaeberry: a favourite food of the capercaillie   © Laurie Campbell

Capercaillie droppings can be DNA tested to identify individuals   © Laurie Campbell

Preparing capercaillie feathers for DNA extraction   © RZSS WildGenes Laboratory

by doing DNA tests on capercaillie droppings found in the forest. By testing each sample with a panel of ten 'microsatellite markers' (sections of repetitive DNA of variable length), it was possible to identify individual capercaillies.

In the Bohemian Forest study, the scientists and their volunteers collected so many samples (7,500) that it was possible to work out the population size (about 500 individuals). It was also possible to get some information about how far they had moved during the period of the study, because 86% of the individuals were recorded at least twice, in different places. Some of them had moved more than 20km, which helps to explain why this population also shows evidence of 'gene flow' between different parts of the forest.

At the time of writing this book, a team from the Royal Zoological Society of Scotland (RZSS) and the Game and Wildlife Conservation Trust (GWCT) had just started a new project using similar methods, to try and improve understanding of the capercaillie population in Scotland. In this project, the team is analysing feathers collected by fieldworkers. It is often possible to get DNA 'fingerprints' from feathers, as well as droppings.

Link to RZSS WildGenes blog post about capercaillie DNA project in Scotland: https://tinyurl.com/y9o3fnxt

The following link provides more information about the capercaillie, including a video clip:
**www.rspb.org.uk/birds-and-wildlife/
wildlife-guides/bird-a-z/capercaillie**

11
Great crested newt

THE GREAT CRESTED NEWT IS AN IMPRESSIVE AMPHIBIAN TO FIND, WITH A BRIGHT ORANGE BELLY AND A DINOSAUR-LIKE CREST, IF IT IS A MALE IN THE BREEDING SEASON. ALTHOUGH IT IS WELL-LOVED BY WILDLIFE ENTHUSIASTS, CONSTRUCTION COMPANIES ARE NOT VERY PLEASED IF IT IS FOUND ON LAND THAT THEY ARE HOPING TO BUILD ON.

Adult male great crested newt, with orange and black belly © Chris Dresh

Adult male great crested newt in a pond near Inverness   © Pete Minting

The great crested newt is often found on the edges of towns and cities, as well as in the countryside. It usually breeds in small lowland ponds, away from large rivers or lochs which contain fish, because fish like to eat newts. Old industrial sites can provide excellent habitat for newts, if fish-free ponds have formed in open areas without dense woodland. Construction companies (particularly housing developers) often go for the same areas, because they are also trying to find land which is unlikely to be flooded by a river and woodlands are often legally protected against development. But great crested newts are also legally protected, which means that (among other things) developers cannot destroy their habitat, unless permission is given by the government.

GREAT CRESTED NEWTS ARE LEGALLY PROTECTED, WHICH MEANS THAT (AMONG OTHER THINGS) DEVELOPERS CANNOT DESTROY THEIR HABITAT, UNLESS PERMISSION IS GIVEN BY THE GOVERNMENT.

It is easy to find newspaper articles which argue against the protection of great crested newts. But these articles rarely point out that the protection of great crested newt sites helps to prevent the loss of green space and gives other, less well-protected wildlife a chance to exist in urban areas. Green (and blue – i.e. water) space is vital for the physical and mental health of people, especially those who live in towns or cities and rarely have a chance to visit the wider countryside.

Are great crested newts only found in Britain?

Great crested newts are found across much of northern Europe, from mainland Britain to western Russia. In south-eastern Europe and western Asia, several closely-related and similar-looking newts are found instead of great crested newts (including Italian, Macedonian and Persian crested newts).

Given that great crested newts have such a wide distribution, it might seem strange that they would be so highly protected in Britain, by the Wildlife and Countryside Act since 1981 and

Great crested newt larva with bushy gills   © Pete Minting

more recently as a European Protected Species. But Britain is a stronghold for great crested newts, partly because in mainland Europe they have to compete with a wider range of amphibian species. Only a few amphibians colonised Britain after the last ice age, before the expansion of the English Channel separated Britain from mainland Europe about 8,500 years ago. There are only seven native amphibians on the British mainland but just across the Channel, there are 16 in northern France.

In Scotland, great crested newts are much less common than they are in England or Wales. You can find them in three main areas of Scotland; southern Scotland (mainly in Dumfries and Galloway and the Borders), the Central Belt from Edinburgh to Glasgow and the inner Moray Firth area, near Inverness. Great crested newts are rarely found high up in the mountains in Scotland, partly because they need fairly warm water to breed in. Many ponds in the Scottish Highlands are also too acidic for great crested newt larvae, due to the chemistry of the soils and rocks in this region. The great crested newt is the second-rarest native amphibian in

Scotland. Only the natterjack toad is rarer (in Scotland, the natterjack toad is only found on the Solway coast near Dumfries).

What do great crested newts look like?

Adult newts have four legs and a tail and look a bit like lizards, but they move slowly and prefer to be in ponds or damp places, whereas lizards are fast-moving and sunbathe to warm up. Great crested newts are much larger than the 'common' species of newt in Britain (palmate and smooth newts). The body of a full-grown great crested newt (excluding the tail) is about the size of an adult person's thumb, compared to someone's little finger for the body of a palmate or smooth newt.

Great crested newts are black or dark grey on top but underneath they have a striking black and orange (or yellow) belly pattern. Adult males have a ragged crest along their back, which they use to display to females. Females do not have a crest but are of similar size and colour.

A newt tadpole is usually called a 'newt larva' (plural; larvae). They can often be seen in ponds, or caught with

Great crested newt larva (black tail blotches) and palmate newt larvae © Pete Minting

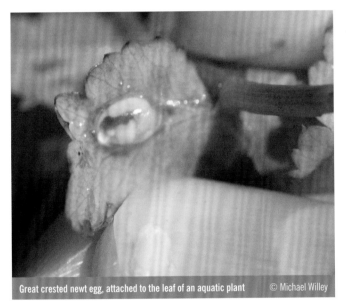

Great crested newt egg, attached to the leaf of an aquatic plant © Michael Willey

FEMALE GREAT CRESTED NEWTS LAY THEIR EGGS ONE AT A TIME AND ATTACH THEM TO AQUATIC PLANTS.

You can find out more about newts and other amphibians at:
www.arc-trust.org/Pages/Category/newts

If I find a great crested newt, what should I do?

Because great crested newts are a highly-protected species, you should have a licence from Scottish Natural Heritage (SNH) before handling or photographing them. However, if you find a newt and think it might be a great crested newt, please take a photograph if you have the chance to do so without disturbing it and enter your record on **www.recordpool.org.uk**. Once great crested newt sites have been discovered, there is a better chance that they will be protected.

Testing pond water for great crested newt DNA

It is now possible to test water samples for the presence of great crested newt DNA. If samples are collected from the environment for DNA testing, such as soil or water, this is called 'environmental DNA' or eDNA testing. This can be done during the day, which makes life easier for people trying to detect newts, especially if it is not possible to visit ponds at night, when newts are most active. You also do not need a protected-species licence to collect water samples, whereas you do need one for other methods of surveying at sites where great crested newts are known to be present.

a net, along with other pond life. Unlike frog and toad tadpoles, newt larvae have bushy gills on the sides of their heads. Great crested newt larvae are the biggest newt larvae found in the wild in Britain and have black blotches on their tails, unlike the larvae of palmate and smooth newts. Female great crested newts lay their eggs one at a time and attach them to aquatic plants.

'Torching' for newts at night in the spring © Laura White, Sustrans

One of the best ways to find newts is to visit ponds in the dark, during the breeding season. If you shine a torch into a pond at night in March, April or May you will have a good chance of seeing newts breeding (and other amphibians, such as frogs and toads). You do not need a protected-species licence to do this, unless it is already known that great crested newts are present.

During the day newts usually remain hidden, to avoid being eaten by predators (such as herons) that stalk the edges of ponds in daylight. It can be perfectly safe to visit ponds at night (as long as safety checks are done beforehand, during the day) but some people do not like going out in the dark and sometimes it is tricky, for instance if there are steep slopes or trip hazards to contend with.

Many wildlife charities need volunteers to help them collect information because there is not enough funding to do professional surveys of wildlife every year. In 2016 and 2017, the Amphibian and Reptile Conservation (ARC) Trust provided volunteers across Scotland with eDNA sampling kits for

A licence is needed to catch or disturb great crested newts © Laura White, Sustrans

detecting great crested newts. Volunteers were keen to try out the new kits and collected samples from a total of 102 sites. The analysis of the samples was done by the same laboratory which did the work when the method was being tested in England and Wales. This meant that the results from Scotland

Rhian Davies collecting a water sample for eDNA analysis

could be directly compared with those from England and Wales.

A test for detecting great crested newt DNA in water samples was first published in 2012. This test checks for the presence of an 81 nucleobase-pair sequence of mitochondrial DNA, which is only found in great crested newts. Whenever a test like this is developed, it is important to check that it is species-specific, i.e. it only detects the 'target' species. If the DNA test accidentally detects another 'non-target' species, it will create 'false positive' results.

The test also needs to be sensitive, i.e. it should be able to detect the target species in environments where it is present, or has been present very recently. Otherwise it may fail to detect the target species, leading to a wrong conclusion that it is absent from the site sampled (a 'false negative').

What did the results from Scotland show?

Several new great crested newt breeding ponds were detected in Scotland by volunteers and ARC staff, using eDNA kits and other survey techniques. Most of the positive results were from within the known range of great crested newts in Scotland but some were in areas where great crested newts had not been officially recorded before. These included ponds near Stranraer in south-west Scotland (in and around the Castle Kennedy Estate) and between Dunbar and Berwick-upon-Tweed in south-east Scotland. Volunteers also detected 'new' breeding sites near Galashiels in the Borders, Cummertrees near Dumfries and Strathpeffer, near Inverness.

Great crested newt by a pond, Hannah Dibdin, Arbroath Academy

Volunteer Sara Pintado Mira, who collected the positive eDNA sample at Cummertrees

Cummertrees Mill Pond near Dumfries; a 'new' great crested newt site

eDNA samples were also taken at sites where great crested newts were already known to breed. This was to check the reliability of the eDNA test. The results from these 'positive control' sites showed that the eDNA test did not always manage to detect great crested newts. A third (33%) of the positive controls (6 of 18) tested negative. This is a higher rate of 'false negatives' than recorded in England and Wales, where only 20 (8%) of 239 'known' great crested newt ponds tested negative.

The success of this project shows that eDNA sampling is a good way of getting volunteers involved in surveying and giving them a better chance to detect a rare species, without having to go out at night, or having to apply for a rare species licence. However, eDNA sampling will not completely replace 'traditional' methods such as torching in the future, because these can be more effective and cheaper (and much more exciting, if you are interested in seeing newts!).

A single negative result from eDNA sampling should not be used to conclude that great crested newts are absent. Scientists have worked out that up to six survey visits are needed to be confident about the absence of great crested newts from a site, using traditional methods such as torching. Evidence from this latest study by ARC shows that (in Scotland, at least) eDNA sampling can result in a fairly high rate of false negatives. More work is needed to find out why there is a higher rate of false negatives in Scotland than in England and Wales. There may be other explanations but it is possible that great crested newts are less abundant in Scottish ponds, resulting in smaller amounts of great crested newt DNA in the water and a failure to collect or detect it.

More details on the Great Crested Newt Detectives project can be seen at: **www.arc-trust.org/gcn-detectives**

Are great crested newts native to the Inverness area?

Another recent (2013) study of great crested newts in Scotland has produced some interesting results. For years, wildlife experts thought that the great crested newt populations in the Inverness area had been introduced by people, partly because they are separated by a long distance (approximately 80 km) from other

Great crested newt by Holly Dargie, Arbroath Academy

great crested newt populations in Scotland. However, DNA evidence (from great crested newts in Scotland and elsewhere) suggests that they may have colonised this area themselves.

If great crested newts were introduced to the Inverness area during the last 100 years, there would almost certainly have been DNA evidence of a 'population bottleneck' in the samples collected from this area. This is because when a population is introduced to a new area, it is usually founded by a small number of individuals. But the DNA analysis (by the University of Salford) did not show any evidence of a recent bottleneck. If several recent introductions had taken place, this might have explained the lack of a bottleneck but great crested newts from Inverness also have 'unique' versions of some genes, which have only been found in great crested newts from this area.

This evidence suggests that the great crested newts found near Inverness probably colonised this area a long time ago. This might have happened between 3,000 and 7,000 years ago, when temperatures in north-western Europe

(including Scotland) were (at times) slightly warmer, or during a period when there was more suitable habitat for great crested newts in Scotland.

Theoretically, people could have introduced great crested newts to the Inverness area in ancient times (as with the Orkney vole, which appears to have been brought by people to the Orkney islands in Scotland from mainland Europe, between 8,000 and 5,000 years ago). But at the moment, there is no evidence that prehistoric people transported great crested newts.

A report on this study (Scottish Natural Heritage report no: 570) can be downloaded from:
www.snh.org.uk/pdfs/publications/ commissioned_reports/570.pdf

A detailed book on the *Amphibians and Reptiles of Scotland* can be downloaded for free from the Glasgow Natural History Society website, at:
www.glasgownaturalhistory.org.uk/ books.html

You can find out more about work that is being done to help British amphibians and reptiles at:
www.arc-trust.org

12
Common frog

THERE ARE ONLY THREE NATIVE AMPHIBIANS IN SCOTLAND WHICH, AS ADULTS, DO NOT HAVE A TAIL; THE COMMON FROG, THE COMMON TOAD AND THE NATTERJACK TOAD. THE COMMON FROG IS THE ONLY ONE WHICH HAS A POWERFUL JUMP AND A SLIPPERY SKIN, WHICH MAKES IT DIFFICULT TO CATCH BY HAND.

Adult common frog   © Fred Holmes

The common toad has a dry and warty skin   © Pete Minting

The natterjack toad has a yellow stripe on its back   © Pete Minting

COMMON FROG BONES HAVE BEEN FOUND ON THE ORKNEY ISLANDS WHICH DATE FROM THE NEOLITHIC PERIOD, AT LEAST 4,000 YEARS AGO. NEOLITHIC PEOPLE MAY HAVE TAKEN THEM THERE TO CREATE A SOURCE OF FOOD.

The common frog is Scotland's most widespread amphibian. Most people in Scotland have seen a common frog, or at least some frog spawn. The common toad is also fairly widespread but in Scotland, the natterjack toad is only found on the Solway coast near Dumfries.

The common frog is found across the Scottish mainland and is present on many Scottish islands. It is not native to many of the islands, especially remote islands. Records suggest that common frogs were first introduced to the Shetlands in the 1800s. Common frog bones have been found on the Orkney islands which date from the Neolithic period, at least 4,000 years ago. Neolithic people may have taken them there to create a source of food. There have been several more introductions since then. In many cases, this has been deliberate because people often like to have frogs in their local area.

Common frogs can be a variety of different colours. Typically the upper body is olive-brown with a few dark markings but you can also find individuals which are largely yellow, black, grey or even brick-red in colour. The underside of the body is usually pale white, yellow or grey. During the breeding season, male common frogs often turn grey and in general, females are browner.

Dark-coloured common frog from Wester Ross © Peter Cunningham

Common frogs can also be red in colour © Fred Holmes

Male common frogs are often greyer when breeding © Tony Gent

■

IF YOU LISTEN CAREFULLY, YOU MAY HEAR MALE COMMON FROGS CALLING IN PONDS DURING THE SPRING (THEY MAKE A SOFT 'CHURRING' SOUND), SOMETIMES DURING THE DAY AS WELL AS AT NIGHT.

The common frog also has a noticeable 'eye-mask' or dark stripe that runs across the eye and in adult frogs, the circular eardrum is clearly visible (not visible in common toads or natterjack toads). If a common frog is resting on the ground, you can often see a hump in its lower back. This is normal and is due to the shape of the frog's pelvis, which is adapted for jumping.

In most of mainland Scotland, if you make a new pond, or if a new flooded area forms in a field or wood, common frogs will often find it and spawn in it the following year. The common frog is the only amphibian in Scotland which lays its spawn in clumps. Common toads and natterjack toads lay their spawn in strings and the newts which are native to Scotland lay their eggs one at a time, usually attaching them to aquatic plants (see separate chapter on the great crested newt).

In Scotland, the common frog is often the first amphibian to spawn (typically in early February). Common frog spawn is fairly resistant to frost but sometimes it will die if there is a very long cold period. If you listen carefully, you may hear male common frogs calling in ponds during the spring (they make a soft 'churring' sound), sometimes during the day as well as at night.

A clump of common frog spawn can contain up to 2,000 eggs. Females

Adult common frogs in a pond at spawning time © Erik Paterson

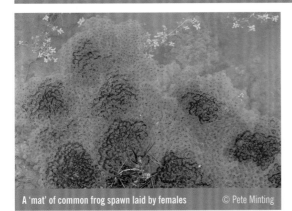
A 'mat' of common frog spawn laid by females © Pete Minting

Common frog spawn about to hatch © Erik Paterson

Common frog tadpole with 'mottled bronze' markings © Erik Paterson

A common 'froglet' emerging from a pond © Pete Minting

THE COMMON FROG

by Aiden Phommavanh, Monymusk Primary School, Inverurie

One day a frog named Bob wanted to jump to the moon. Sounds like a strange thing to want to do but all his family had done it. He wondered how they had managed to do it but they never told him. Bob was a common frog (which is one of five thousand species of frog!).

Bob lived with his family in a pond. One of the reasons he wanted to go to the moon was because his family had made him stay in the pond for his whole life. His older brothers and sisters teased him for being the only one in the family that hadn't been to the moon, which made Bob very upset. But he believed that he could go to the moon one day because Bob remembered what his grandpa had said to him (before he got crushed by a car). He said "follow your dreams and never give up!"

often lay their spawn next to other clumps, resulting in a spawn 'mat' which can contain hundreds of clumps. Common frog spawn usually floats and the 'embryos' within the eggs develop rapidly into tadpoles in mild weather. The tadpoles are less than 1 cm long and almost black when they hatch but by the time they start to grow legs (back legs first) they can be 4 cm long. At this stage, they are 'mottled bronze' in colour.

At first, common frog tadpoles feed largely on tiny plants (algae) but later on they also feed on dead animals (such as earthworms that fall into a pond) which helps them to get enough protein to complete their development. After their front legs have developed, the tail starts to be reabsorbed into the body and disappear. The majority of common

frog tadpoles emerge as froglets during July and August in Scotland but some of them overwinter in ponds and emerge the following summer.

Why have all the tadpoles in my pond disappeared?

People often ask me why all the tadpoles in their garden pond have disappeared, or why there are not as many frogs as there used to be. There are several possibilities but if the tadpoles have disappeared, it could just be that they have emerged (turned into froglets) and dispersed away from the pond. This is possible in Scotland by August but it is unlikely before July.

Often the reason is that the pond in question is now a few years old and has acquired a population of predatory insects. New ponds are often good news for amphibians because they do not contain predators. After a few years, a healthy pond in Scotland will usually acquire a population of great diving beetles. The larvae of these beetles (and other insects, such as dragonflies)

Did you know?

The Scots name for the common frog is 'puddock' and some places in Scotland, such as the Paddock Burn near Peebles, may have been named after frogs.

Adult common frog in a pond © Jim Foster

hunt tadpoles. These insects try to stay hidden in pond weed or at the bottom of the pond during the day, so you might not see them. The number of tadpoles and frogs may go downhill as a result of predation but this is not necessarily a bad thing, if a greater variety of life now exists in your pond. Adult and juvenile common frogs are also important prey items for many other native species, such as herons and otters.

Diseases can sometimes have a bad effect on frog populations. A virus called *Ranavirus* sometimes kills common frogs. Common frogs with *Ranavirus* often have skin ulcers. This virus also infects fish and reptiles and it may have been accidentally introduced to Britain from another country. So far, the majority of *Ranavirus* outbreaks in Britain have been in England.

Pollution is rarely a problem for garden ponds but it is not advisable to use artificial fertilisers or pesticides, if you would like your garden to be useful for wildlife. If you use fertilisers, your pond may be choked by an excessive growth of green algae. Most adult amphibians (including common frogs) eat small animals (such as earthworms, insects, slugs) which are killed by pesticides. The use of pesticides is one of the reasons for the ongoing global decline in the abundance of wildlife.

Adult frogs need habitat on land, as well as ponds. If your garden used to border open countryside but is now next to a motorway or surrounded by a new housing estate, it may be harder for 'your' frogs to find food, migrate to other ponds or hibernate safely during the winter.

Common frog tadpoles in an aquarium © Erik Paterson

Tadpoles in the classroom – legal but controversial

Today, there is often disagreement about whether people should help or allow children to catch tadpoles, keep them and watch them grow in captivity. It is now rare to see tadpoles in a classroom but children enjoy seeing tadpoles develop and it can help people to develop an interest in science. But animal welfare organisations have argued that tadpoles should not be kept in classrooms, because it is difficult to maintain suitable conditions for common frogs inside a heated building.

It is legal to capture common frog tadpoles and keep them in captivity but it does take dedication and suitable equipment to keep them healthy indoors for several weeks. An alternative option might be the creation of a wildlife garden, including a shallow pond and outdoor study area, where children can pond dip and study pond life outdoors. Common frogs can survive in towns and cities, as long as there are areas of green and 'blue' (water) space that are reasonably well-connected.

Hoping to study an amphibian? Frogs could be the answer

Scientists have done many studies of common frogs. This is partly because common frogs are so widespread and relatively easy to study. The common frog is not a highly-protected species in Britain and although it is illegal to buy or sell them, it is legal to keep them captive, provided that adequate steps are taken to look after them (in line with the Animal Welfare Act, 2006).

In the common frog, large spawning events are most likely to occur at, or around full moon. The breeding cycle of many other amphibians is linked to the phases of the moon or 'lunar cycle'. Some of them also tend to breed at full moon but others breed at around the 'new' moon when most of the moon is dark and barely visible. Some do not appear to breed at a particular phase of the moon and respond most

Common frog by Kyle Diack, Greenfaulds High School

strongly to the weather. The responses of amphibians to the moon are probably encoded in their DNA and have been passed down many generations.

In other studies, scientists have tried to find out if there is a genetic basis to the rate at which tadpoles develop. There is strong 'selection pressure' for the tadpoles of many amphibians to develop rapidly. In northern Europe, many species of amphibian struggle to survive unless they emerge early from ponds and find enough food to fatten themselves up before winter.

In one study, scientists moved common frog tadpoles from the far north of Finland to southern Sweden (and vice versa). This was to find out if the tadpoles would develop at a different rate, if they were moved, or if they would just develop at the same rate as usual. Interestingly, the tadpoles kept to their normal development rates. For example, tadpoles from northern Finland developed 10 days faster than those from the south, when tadpoles from both places were kept in the same conditions in southern Sweden. Northern Finland has a shorter summer compared to southern Sweden, so tadpoles from the north probably need to develop faster, if they are going to turn into froglets before winter. In this study, the scientists concluded that this difference in development rate must also be 'genetic' or encoded in the frog's DNA.

Common frog by Michael Prentice, Kirkintilloch High School

Scientists at the University of Glasgow have reached similar conclusions when studying common frogs in Scotland. They have also found that common frog populations in Scotland are fairly well-mixed, genetically, compared to common frog populations in some parts of mainland Europe. This seems to suggest that common frogs in Scotland have moved around a lot and, at the moment, they exist as a fairly well-connected population, or series of connected populations.

Another study has suggested that the common frog might have survived in southern Ireland during the ice ages, which ended about 15,000 years ago. This is interesting because many animals that are native to Britain (including Scotland) recolonised this part of Europe after the last ice age

from much further south, from ice-age 'refuges' in southern Europe. But common frogs in southern Ireland have unusual 'mitochondrial DNA haplotypes' which might indicate that they survived in Ireland. Common frogs from other parts of Britain (including Scotland) have similar haplotypes to other common frogs in western Europe and probably survived the ice ages in a refuge further south.

A detailed book on the *Amphibians and Reptiles of Scotland* can be downloaded for free from the Glasgow Natural History Society website, at: **www.glasgownaturalhistory.org.uk/books.html**

You can find out more about work that is being done to help British amphibians and reptiles at: **www.arc-trust.org**

MANY ANIMALS THAT ARE NATIVE TO BRITAIN (INCLUDING SCOTLAND) RECOLONISED THIS PART OF EUROPE AFTER THE LAST ICE AGE FROM MUCH FURTHER SOUTH, FROM ICE-AGE 'REFUGES' IN SOUTHERN EUROPE.

13
Adder

THE ADDER IS THE ONLY VENOMOUS SNAKE IN BRITAIN. LIKE MOST OTHER VENOMOUS SNAKES, IT HAS A BAD REPUTATION. BUT IT IS A SHY ANIMAL AND RARELY BITES PEOPLE, UNLESS IT IS PICKED UP, HARASSED OR TRODDEN ON. THE ADDER HAS EXCELLENT CAMOUFLAGE AND IF YOU HAVE SPENT MUCH TIME OUTDOORS IN SCOTLAND, YOU MAY HAVE WALKED PAST ONE, OR HAD A PICNIC, WITHIN A FEW METRES OF THIS MASTER OF DISGUISE.

Male adder

© Fred Holmes

Male adder © Chris Dresh

IF YOU SEE A SNAKE WITH ZIG-ZAG MARKINGS (OR IS VERY DARK IN COLOUR – SOME ADDERS ARE BLACK), IT IS SAFEST TO ASSUME THAT IT IS AN ADDER AND LEAVE IT ALONE.

The adder is the only native snake in Britain which has a zig-zag pattern on its back. The only other wild snake that you might find in Scotland (the non-venomous grass snake) is extremely rare here and does not have a zig-zag pattern. You are more likely to find a legless lizard (called the slow worm), which looks a bit like a snake but the slow worm also does not have any zig-zag markings and, like the grass snake, it is completely harmless.

A typical adder, seen basking on a roadside verge © Pete Minting

Adders have unique, individual head patterns © Chris Dresh

If you see a snake with zig-zag markings (or is very dark in colour – some adders are black), it is safest to assume that it is an adder and leave it alone. It is illegal to kill or deliberately harm adders, or destroy their habitat. It is also illegal to keep them in captivity, unless you have a licence to do so.

Are adders dangerous?

It is true that an adder can give you a painful bite, often with unpleasant side effects, but it is unlikely to kill you. Some people can have an unusually strong reaction to adder venom and this is dangerous, so it is important to go to a hospital (at a safe speed!) if you do get bitten.

Adders usually avoid people but they may bite you if you pick them up, repeatedly disturb them at close range, or accidentally tread on them. If you

If you are bitten by an adder, DO NOT cut the wound, apply a tourniquet or attempt to suck out the venom; these actions would have no beneficial effect and could be more dangerous than the bite.

have a dog, it is best to keep your dog on a lead if you are in a place where adders are known to be present, or in habitat that looks suitable for them. Dogs often leap about in vegetation at the side of paths, where adders like to bask. It is also a good idea for people to wear boots and trousers in areas with adders, rather than shorts and sandals.

Hiding in plain sight

At one of the adder sites I have visited in Scotland, there must be at least a hundred adders, based on photographs of their head patterns (adders have unique, individual patterns on their heads). But the site's owner has only seen an adder on a couple of occasions, despite living there for years.

Last year I was speaking to a roads maintenance team, by the side of a road, and I asked them if they had seen any snakes or lizards. The leader of the team replied that he had been working in the area for 20 years and had not seen any. After the team had finished working and gone home, I got photos of six adders basking on the verge, right next to the

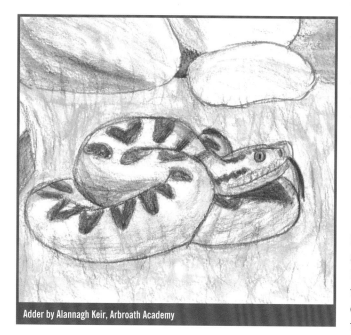

Adder by Alannagh Keir, Arbroath Academy

REPTILES USUALLY USE EXTERNAL
SOURCES OF HEAT (SUCH AS
THE SUN) TO RAISE THEIR BODY
TEMPERATURE BUT MANY OF
THEM CAN ALSO CREATE HEAT BY
FLEXING THEIR MUSCLES.

road where we had been talking.

Adders often bask on rocky banks and
verges. If the ground is partly overgrown
by brambles, the spiky brambles provide
the adders with another line of defence
against predators and people. Adders are
difficult to spot against backgrounds of
similar colour, such as dead vegetation
or rocks.

Soaking up the sun

Adders often flatten their bodies when
basking in the sun, to try and absorb as
much heat as possible. They will also
make use of heat from objects that have
been left lying on the ground, such as
pieces of metal roofing, which heat up
in the sun more rapidly than natural
materials.

Reptiles are often described as
'cold-blooded'. This is misleading,
because their blood is not usually
that cold, unless they are hibernating
(asleep in winter). Reptiles usually use
external sources of heat (such as the
sun) to raise their body temperature
but many of them can also create heat

by flexing their muscles. Unlike birds
and mammals, reptiles do not generate
heat from the digestion of their food, so
they find it hard to remain active in cold
conditions but some of them are able
to survive in places where it is cold for
much of the year. In mainland Europe,
the adder (along with the common or
viviparous lizard, which is also found in
Scotland) is found as far north as the
Arctic circle.

Like many other reptiles which are
able to survive in cold environments,
the adder does not lay eggs but gives
birth to live, fully developed young. It is
particularly important for female adders
to keep their bodies warm during the
breeding season, if they are pregnant or
'gravid'. Gravid females need additional
warmth to ensure that the baby adders
developing inside their bodies grow
properly and are born at a time of year
(usually in the late summer or autumn)
when they are able to find food.

In Scotland, adders typically hibernate
underground from October to February
but they can become active and emerge
from their hiding places at any time of
year, if the air temperature exceeds 10 °C.

Ancient adder history

The adder or 'common viper' is one of
the most widely-distributed vipers in the
world and is found in much of Europe

Male adders (usually silver or grey in the breeding season) often guard females (usually brown)   © Rodger McPhail

Radio-tracking studies in England have shown that adders spend a lot of time underground, often in burrows made by other animals. I have seen an adder disappear into a vole burrow on a grassy bank but then reappear out of a different hole several metres away.

and northern Asia. Like many other animals mentioned in this book, the adder has colonised Britain more than once. It originally colonised what is now Britain (including Scotland) about one million years ago but was forced south during several ice ages. After the end of the last ice age, about 15,000 years ago, adders returned to Britain from an ice age 'refuge' in central Europe, before the expansion of the English Channel separated Britain from mainland Europe. DNA evidence (collected from adders across Europe) suggests that the ice age

refuge for the adders which are found today in Britain was in central or eastern Europe, north of the Alps. Many other less 'cold-tolerant' species survived in refuges much further south.

Adders are found south of the Alps in mainland Europe (in Italy and the Balkans) but they are slightly different from those in northern Europe and some of them are regarded as separate subspecies (such as the Bosnian adder). There are also several other species of viper in southern Europe (such as Seoane's viper, the meadow viper, European asp and horned viper). The adder is quite closely-related to these species and looks similar to them. Vipers have existed for at least 50 million years and today, worldwide, there are more than 300 species of viper (including pit vipers).

Adders sometimes get run over on rural roads and tracks

ADDERS CAN THRIVE IN A VARIETY OF HABITATS. IN SCOTLAND, I HAVE OFTEN SEEN ADDERS IN AREAS OF PEATY, BOGGY HEATHLAND (OFTEN CALLED 'MOSSES') BUT ALSO ON CLIFFS, SCREE SLOPES, SAND DUNES, RAILWAY EMBANKMENTS AND ROADSIDE VERGES.

Adders in Scotland

Scotland has many populations of adders but they are patchily-distributed and they are rarely seen in cities or town centres. The adder has been persecuted for centuries in Scotland and it has only recently been protected (under the Wildlife and Countryside Act, 1981, as amended for Scotland).

A major landowner visited my stand at the Highland Show in 2014 and proudly announced, on seeing a picture of an adder, that "we kill hundreds of those on our estate every year!" Clearly, despite the legislation, persecution has not completely stopped but hopefully our educational work will encourage people to value the adder as a native species. Adders have disappeared from many

parts of England and Wales and they may be extinct in parts of Scotland, such as the Pentland Hills near Edinburgh, where they existed until fairly recently.

In Scotland, adders can be found on the mainland and some of the larger islands, including Mull, Skye, Jura, Islay and Arran. On the mainland, Dumfries and Galloway, the Borders, the Cairngorms and the Loch Lomond area are thought to be strongholds for the adder but they are found in many other places and it is possible that many populations in remote areas have not been recorded.

Adders can thrive in a variety of habitats. In Scotland, I have often seen adders in areas of peaty, boggy heathland (often called 'mosses') but also on cliffs, scree slopes, sand dunes, railway embankments and roadside verges. I only know of one site where someone has adders in their garden (in a rockery). Adders do not like to be disturbed, partly because this prevents them from basking. It can be very difficult to tell where they hibernate,

© Rhona Anderson

ADDER

by Ella Moroney-Lavin, Edinburgh

Adders lurk in the rough
valleys of the highlands,
Dark zig-zag patterns
slipping through those
unforgiving bad lands.
Dancing with voles in a
fiery fight,
Ending their miserable
attempts with a swift bite.
Reigning with terror across
the gruelling countryside.

unless you keep a close eye on them in the autumn and again in the spring, when they re-emerge from their hibernation sites.

DNA studies and genetics

Luckily there is no need to touch an adder, in order to collect an adder DNA sample. Snakes shed or 'slough' their skin at regular intervals and you should be able to find shed adder skins on the ground at sites with plenty of adders. The skin is often left on top of coarse vegetation, such as heather, which the adder uses to help pull off the skin, like peeling off a sock. DNA can usually be extracted from a sloughed adder skin, if it has been collected and stored in a cool, dry dark place.

No detailed research has been done on the genetics of adders in Scotland. To date, the majority of DNA-based research on adders has depended upon samples from mainland Europe, with a small number of samples from England. Consequently, we are trying to build a 'library' of shed adder skins from across

Scotland, in the hope that we will be able to find funding for a DNA study.

It would be interesting to study the genetics of adders in Scotland, particularly those which appear to belong to isolated populations on

Shed adder skins can be DNA-tested   © Pete Minting

Adders often prey on rodents, such as voles   © Rodger McPhail

islands, or in small patches of suitable habitat. It is possible that some populations will be suffering from inbreeding, if they have been through a 'population bottleneck' when only a few individuals have survived to pass on their genes.

In mainland Europe, inbreeding has resulted in problems for some isolated populations of adders. In 1996, scientists reported that a small population of adders (with less than 40 adult adders) in Sweden was suffering from inbreeding. Female adders from this population gave birth to unusually

Adders prey on a variety of small animals, including rodents such as mice and voles. Their diet varies quite widely, according to the habitat they are in. They also eat lizards, small birds and amphibians. The first prey for a young adder is often a small lizard.

low numbers of young, with a poor survival rate. In 1999, the scientists introduced 20 male adders from another population. In 2004, the scientists reported a dramatic improvement in adder breeding success at the Swedish site, which may have been due to an increase in genetic diversity.

Inbreeding does not always result in a reduction in breeding success. But female adders often mate with multiple males during a breeding season and give birth to young with several different fathers. This may suggest that genetic diversity is useful in this species, because otherwise, we might expect females to avoid wasting good basking time and energy by mating with several males.

Earlier in this chapter, I mentioned that DNA-based research was used to work out where adders survived in Europe during the ice ages, thousands

Female adder © Chris Dresh

Juvenile adders are often brick-red © John Baker

ADDER OR SUBTRACTOR?

by Craig McCowan, Ardnamurchan High School

Addy the adder loved maths
It made him hiss with delight!
He added and subtracted
Morning, noon and night.
He counted all the things he saw
on the forest floor.
Like leaves, nuts and flowers
until he could count no more.
He stumbled on a stack of nuts
as tall as the Eiffel Tower.
And his eyes popped out in sheer delight
He tried to take away 10 nuts from the bottom row,
but all at once the nuts crashed down
onto his head below.
And now he said "though nuts are rife
Subtracting is not for me.
I want to live a longer life,
so an adder I shall be!"

of years ago. In that study, the scientists looked at the mitochondrial DNA (mtDNA) of adders across Europe, including a couple of sites in England. If DNA research on adders is extended to Scotland, mtDNA analysis might be the first 'port of call'.

In order to do more fine-scale population analysis, we might need to look at nuclear DNA, rather than mtDNA, perhaps using microsatellites or single-nucleotide polymorphisms (SNPs). That would allow us to find out more about the history of adders in Britain and help us to find out if Scottish adders are likely to be suffering from inbreeding.

If you would like to help us with this work, please collect any shed adder skins (or bits of skin) that you find at sites in Scotland (or England, near the border with Scotland). Please be careful and wear suitable clothing at adder sites, as described above. If you find an adder skin, please store it in a paper envelope

Snakes detect the scent of other animals using their forked tongue © Fred Holmes

marked with the date of collection, site name, collector's name and an accurate grid reference. Please post the envelopes (ideally, inside another strong envelope or jiffy bag) to:

ARC Genebank
655A Christchurch Road
Boscombe
Bournemouth
BH1 4AP.

A detailed book on the *Amphibians and Reptiles of Scotland*, which includes more information about adders, can be downloaded for free from the Glasgow Natural History Society website, at: **www.glasgownaturalhistory.org.uk/ books.html**

You can find out more about work that is being done to help British reptiles and amphibians at: **www.arc-trust.org**

IF YOU WOULD LIKE TO HELP US WITH THIS WORK, PLEASE COLLECT ANY SHED ADDER SKINS (OR BITS OF SKIN) THAT YOU FIND AT SITES IN SCOTLAND (OR ENGLAND, NEAR THE BORDER WITH SCOTLAND).

14
Atlantic salmon

THE ATLANTIC SALMON HAS MANY TALENTS. IT CAN SWIM THOUSANDS OF KILOMETRES ACROSS THE ATLANTIC OCEAN IN SEARCH OF FOOD AND THEN FIND ITS WAY BACK, TO THE RIVER WHERE IT ORIGINALLY HATCHED. IT CAN LEAP OVER WATERFALLS WHICH ARE HIGHER THAN THE OLYMPIC RECORD FOR THE HIGH JUMP. IT BREEDS IN WATER WHICH IS SO COLD THAT IT WOULD KILL US IN A MATTER OF MINUTES. THIS IS A TRULY AMAZING ANIMAL.

Atlantic salmon trying to leap over a waterfall, on its way 'home' to breed © Laurie Campbell

MOST SALMON, WITH THE EXCEPTION OF A FEW 'LAND-LOCKED'
POPULATIONS, MIGRATE TO THE SEA IN ORDER TO FEED AND GROW
TO ADULT SIZE. ATLANTIC SALMON USUALLY MIGRATE TO THE
ATLANTIC OCEAN FROM THEIR 'HOME' RIVERS WHEN THEY ARE TWO
OR THREE YEARS OLD.

The salmon is one of the best-studied animals on the planet. This is partly because salmon are important to the world's economy, as a source of food. Fishing for salmon using a rod and line (salmon angling) is also a popular sport in many countries. Consequently it is relatively easy for scientists to secure funding to study salmon, compared to many other animals.

Worldwide, there are seven species of fish that are called salmon. These species probably had a common ancestor which existed around 20 million years ago but since then, they have been evolving in different parts of the world. Six of the world's seven salmon species are native to the Pacific Ocean region (pink, chum, coho, masu, sockeye and chinook salmon). The Atlantic salmon is the only salmon species which is native to the Atlantic Ocean region, including Britain and Scotland.

Most salmon, with the exception of a few 'land-locked' populations, migrate

Wild Atlantic salmon eggs are a beautiful pink colour © Laurie Campbell

to the sea in order to feed and grow to adult size. Atlantic salmon usually migrate to the Atlantic Ocean from their 'home' rivers when they are two or three years old. They then spend between one and four years at sea, where they feed on a variety of marine animals and grow rapidly.

Once an Atlantic salmon has reached adult size, it will return to its home river to breed in fresh water. Adults returning to breed usually weigh at least 2 kg but those which have bred more than once can weigh up to 30 kg. The Atlantic salmon usually spawns in a fast-flowing, clean river. The adult female salmon lays her eggs in gravel on the riverbed, burying them in a nest called a 'redd' with her powerful tail. As she lays the eggs, a male salmon fertilises them, by releasing his sperm into the water around them.

In Scotland, Atlantic salmon usually begin spawning in December, or during the first severe frost of the year. At this time, the temperature of the river water is close to freezing. Adult salmon can enter rivers in Scotland as early as May but they do their best to remain hidden (often in deep pools) until spawning time. An adult male salmon can detect the scent of a female salmon many kilometres upstream, so when the females are finally ready to breed, the males are able to find them quickly.

Adult male salmon grow an extended jaw (called a 'kype') during the breeding season, which they use to fight off other males. It has been recently been discovered (with the help of DNA technology) that some of the eggs laid by females are actually fertilised by juvenile male salmon, which are only about 12 cm long and have not yet migrated to the sea. These small 'precocious' males are sometimes killed by adult males, if the adult males spot them trying to fertilise the eggs.

The Atlantic salmon is quite closely-related to two other species of fish that are found in Britain, the brown trout and the Arctic charr. Some brown trout migrate to the sea to feed and are called sea trout (but they are still regarded as the same species).

Adult female salmon caught on a rod and line
© Bob Kindness

Anger or hunger?

It is quite difficult to catch a salmon on a rod and line in a river. This is partly because adult salmon do not feed when they are in fresh water. Salmon anglers often use a brightly-coloured 'fishing fly' or a spinning lure called a 'rapala' as bait. When salmon do take the bait, it may actually be an aggressive response, rather than hunger. When adult salmon are in fresh water, they gradually lose weight and many of them die, due to exhaustion and starvation, once they have spawned.

Bringing nutrients back

Salmon play a vital role in many ecosystems, including the food webs that exist on land. When adult salmon migrate back from the sea to breed, they are often caught by predators and dragged on to land. In Britain, otters often catch salmon that have become weak at the end of their spawning season. In the past, bears would have fed on salmon in Britain, as they still do today in places like Canada.

Studies in north America have shown that the nutrients from wild salmon, brought back on to land by predators, help forests to grow. Today, forestry companies use artificial fertilisers (invented only a hundred years ago) to boost tree growth but it is an intriguing thought that Scotland's ancient forests were helped to grow by the bodies of fish which migrated upstream, thousands of years ago.

Even in the absence of large predators such as bears, the dead bodies of salmon that have spawned are very useful because they are a source of food for other smaller animals, such as aquatic insects, which help to feed other fish, including the next generation of salmon.

Whenever migratory fish such as salmon pass from fresh water into sea water (and back again), they have to cope with rapid changes in the salt content of the water. They have specially-adapted gills, kidneys and skin which allow them to do this very quickly.

Salmon leaping at a waterfall on the River Girvan, Ayrshire © Pete Minting

Decline drives research

Populations of wild Atlantic salmon have declined dramatically since the 1960s. This is due to a combination of factors, including over-fishing (by a variety of methods) and local environmental factors, such as river pollution and loss of habitat. On a global scale, climate change is probably also having an effect. Salmon need cold water to breed in but high temperatures might also have effects at sea. High sea temperatures result in outbreaks of disease in many fish, including salmon. Atlantic salmon are currently found as far south as Portugal in Europe, but the Portuguese population may go extinct, if global temperatures keep rising. Pollution control and habitat restoration projects have allowed some Atlantic salmon populations to recover but this species is still declining across much of its range and there is an urgent need for more research.

DNA and Atlantic salmon

There have been so many genetic studies of Atlantic salmon that it is difficult to decide which ones to mention. Here, I have included just a few examples of how DNA technology is being used to help improve our understanding of this species – if you search online, you will find many others.

Salmon cages in the sea, on the north-west coast of Scotland   © Wester Ross Fisheries Trust

Salmon farming – background

Atlantic salmon are farmed for food in many parts of the world, including Scotland. In salmon farming, young salmon are reared from eggs in freshwater tanks (usually on land) and when they are ready to migrate to the sea, they are transferred to 'sea cages' along the coast, where they grow rapidly, once they are in seawater. Within two or three years, a farmed Atlantic salmon can be 10kg in weight and is worth a great deal of money, when killed and sold for food.

Salmon farming creates many jobs and can provide a major boost to the economy. In parts of Scotland, more people are employed in salmon farming than any other business. However, salmon farming has many effects on wildlife and the environment. Farmed salmon are usually fed pellets which contain oils and proteins derived from wild fish and many other marine organisms (such as 'krill' – animals which are closely-related to shrimps) that are overfished at sea.

Salmon can also carry parasites, including 'sea lice' which multiply rapidly on salmon farms if their numbers are not controlled. Sea lice are often passed on to wild sea trout and salmon, as they migrate past sea cages containing farmed salmon. If a young sea trout acquires more than 30 sea lice, it rarely survives to breed. If pesticides are used to kill the lice, these chemicals can also have bad effects on wildlife, if the amounts used are not strictly controlled.

Sea lice numbers can be controlled by using another fish, called a 'wrasse' which bites the lice off salmon and eats them. However, there is often a shortage of these 'cleaner wrasse' because it is difficult to breed large numbers of them in captivity and wild-caught wrasse can carry viruses, resulting in more disease problems.

The sea cages that farmed salmon are kept in sometimes break open during storms, or are torn open by wild animals such as seals, if they try to catch the salmon inside. Each cage can contain thousands of salmon. If the farmed salmon escape, they are free to migrate into local rivers and mix with wild salmon populations. Farmed salmon are often from a different country. In Scotland, the majority of farmed salmon are of Norwegian origin.

Salmon eggs and milt being
mixed at a hatchery   © Pete Minting

Adult male salmon, collected for use at a hatchery   © Pete Minting

Salmon stocking – background

For more than 100 years in Scotland, people have been rearing young salmon in captivity (in 'salmon hatcheries') and releasing them into local rivers. The aim of this 'salmon stocking' is usually to try and increase the local salmon population, or protect it from extinction.

There are salmon hatcheries on many of the river catchments in Scotland. These hatcheries are mainly run by people with an interest in salmon angling. It is relatively easy to rear young salmon from eggs in captivity, provided that you have access to a supply of clean, cold, oxygenated water. The water supply for a hatchery is usually piped from the river where the stocking takes place.

The hatchery-rearing process works like this; firstly, hatchery staff collect wild salmon eggs (with permission from the authorities) from female adult salmon that have migrated upstream from the sea to breed. The salmon are carefully caught in nets and if the female is 'ripe' her eggs can be gently squeezed into a bucket. Sperm (called milt) can also be collected from adult male salmon and this is mixed with the eggs in the bucket, to fertilise them. The adults are released and the eggs kept in the hatchery, in specially-designed trays, until they have hatched.

Hatchery-reared salmon are usually released a few weeks after they hatch, at the 'fry' stage but sometimes they are reared on to the 'parr' stage, when they are about two years old, 12 cm long and almost ready to migrate to the sea.

On some river catchments, where there is a major obstruction to salmon migration, such as a hydro-electric dam, salmon sometimes cannot reach the upper parts of the catchment without help. Many dams have 'fish passes' added to them, which allow the salmon to migrate upstream (an example of a fish pass can be seen on the River Tay in Scotland, at Pitlochry). But in cases where salmon struggle to get past a man-made obstruction (such as on the River Conon near Inverness), stocking can help to ensure that the upper part of the river catchment still produces salmon, as well as other types of fish which do not need to migrate to the sea.

When young salmon are ready to migrate to sea, they turn silver   © Pete Minting

AMAZING ATLANTIC SALMON

by Euan Dillon, Troqueer Primary School, Dumfries

Sleek bar of silver
Shining so bright
You move rapidly through streams and rivers
Your powerful form glistening in the sunlight
As you swim to the Atlantic

You are elusive
The tiniest of flies does not appeal to you
I try hard to capture you
To observe your beauty and magnificence
But my fight is useless
Long days and nights pass but you still
escape me
It's like you are taunting me

And so I leave empty-handed
You have beaten me
You are free to swim
For now...

EACH FEMALE SALMON LAYS THOUSANDS OF EGGS AND A SALMON RIVER USUALLY CONTAINS HUNDREDS OF ADULT SALMON AT SPAWNING TIME.

Norwegian and Scottish salmon are the same species (Atlantic salmon), so this may not appear to be as serious a problem as hybridisation with a completely different species. However, if we allow Norwegian salmon to keep escaping in large numbers, this is risky, because we cannot predict the effects that this will have on Scotland's native salmon in the long-term.

Dumping of dead salmon

Scientists have developed ways of identifying the origin of dead salmon that have been dumped. Sometimes large numbers of salmon die at salmon farms and it is cheapest for the farm owners to dump the fish (illegally) at sea. In Norway, where there are huge numbers of salmon farms, the Norwegian government has prosecuted salmon farmers for dumping dead salmon and identified the origin of pollution from fish-processing factories, with the help of DNA evidence.

Does stocking work?

There is no evidence that stocking increases the size of the salmon population in a river, unless part of the river to be stocked is above a major obstruction, such as a man-made dam, which prevents the salmon from migrating. When stocking first became popular as a 'management' technique for salmon rivers in Britain, the concept of

Hybridisation with farmed salmon

In 2013, the results of a DNA study (the Managing Interactions with Aquaculture Project) showed that 25% of juvenile wild salmon captured in rivers in north-west Scotland were hybrids between escaped farmed salmon (of Norwegian origin) and native Scottish salmon. This level of hybridisation might have a negative effect on the survival rate of wild salmon. The salmon which are native to Scotland have been adapting to local conditions for thousands of years. The accidental introduction of salmon from Norway could result in a reduction in the survival rate of Scotland's wild salmon, if they are less-well adapted to their local environment, as a result of the hybridisation.

Juvenile salmon do best in clean rivers with lots of boulders © Pete Minting

a 'carrying capacity' for a river, in terms of how much habitat and food it could provide, was not widely understood.

Each female salmon lays thousands of eggs and a salmon river usually contains hundreds of adult salmon at spawning time. The number of young salmon that survive to migrate to the sea is usually more closely related to the conditions in the river, in terms of the food supply and amount of suitable habitat, than the number of young salmon that hatch out, or are stocked into the river.

In a wild river, there are usually a lot more adult salmon than are used for the hatchery. In other words, the hatchery-reared salmon do not have as many different parents, compared to those in the wild – they are less 'genetically diverse'. They may also have become

In fresh water, young salmon feed mainly on insects © Stuart Crofts

accustomed to the hatchery environment and the shock of being released into a river probably kills some of them.

The impacts of salmon stocking on wild salmon populations are difficult to assess. Several scientists have attempted to compare the survival rates of hatchery-reared salmon with those of wild salmon, by a variety of methods,

Tiny wire tag, used for tagging young salmon
© Northwest Marine Technology

including DNA testing and tagging. Most of these studies suggest that the survival rate of hatchery-reared salmon is very low, compared to wild salmon.

It is possible to tag juvenile salmon with tiny 'coded wire' tags, before they migrate to sea. Coded wire tagging has produced some interesting information and some tagged salmon do survive and return to breed. However, it is possible that tagging reduces their survival rate. The tags, which are usually injected into the head of the fish, may interfere with the ability of salmon to migrate.

Another way to assess the success of a stocking programme is to analyse the genetic structure of the population. Stocking of salmon rivers has also taken place in England. For example, the River Dart in Devon was repeatedly stocked with Atlantic salmon from Scotland and Iceland in the 1960s.

In 2008, scientists from the University of Exeter compared the DNA of salmon from the River Dart with the DNA of salmon from the Scottish and Icelandic populations which were used to stock the Dart in the 1960s. Their results showed little evidence of Scottish or Icelandic salmon genes in the Dart population. This suggests that the stocking was not very successful and most of the salmon in the River Dart today are descended from the original population, not Scottish or Icelandic salmon.

River of origin

It is now possible to catch salmon far out in the Atlantic Ocean and find out which river they came from, by testing their DNA. Scientists have collected a 'baseline' or DNA library of genetic information from salmon in their home rivers. When compared against the DNA of an individual salmon caught far out at sea (or in the freezer of a poacher), this information can be used to work out the origin of an individual salmon with a surprisingly high degree of accuracy. Using the DNA of an animal to work

Atlantic salmon leaping by Anthony Ison, Lockerbie Academy

TAGGING STUDIES HAVE SHOWN THAT ATLANTIC SALMON FROM SCOTLAND CAN MIGRATE AS FAR AWAY AS THE COAST OF GREENLAND TO FEED.

out its population of origin is called 'assignment testing'.

The accuracy or 'resolution' of the assignment testing has improved dramatically in the last 15 years. In 2005, scientists from the Scottish government's Fisheries Research Services (FRS) laboratory published a reliable method of identifying the 'broad' origin of Atlantic salmon (whether they had come from a population along the east coast of America, or the west coast of Europe), by using a combination of mitochondrial and microsatellite DNA markers.

In 2010, a team of scientists led by Exeter University used a more detailed panel of microsatellite markers, which made it possible to tell the difference between salmon from two large areas of northern Britain (as well as other parts of Europe). In 2016, an even more detailed study, using single nucleotide polymorphism (SNP) markers was published. This study (led by The Rivers and Lochs Institute in Inverness) made it possible to assign salmon to individual

rivers (including rivers in Scotland), not just broad regions.

There are many ways in which assignment testing could be useful. Although tagging studies have shown that Atlantic salmon from Scotland can migrate as far away as the coast of Greenland to feed, we do not know if salmon from particular rivers tend to feed in a particular part of the Atlantic. In practice, assignment testing means that all wild salmon are tagged when they are born, by the DNA sequences that they inherit from their parents. It is very difficult to sample salmon far out at sea but thanks to the latest advances in DNA technology, we now have a fairly good chance of determining a salmon's origin, even if it has not been tagged using a 'traditional' tagging method.

Suggested links

Atlantic Salmon Trust:
www.atlanticsalmontrust.org

North Atlantic Salmon Conservation Organisation:
www.nasco.int/sas/research.htm

Fisheries Management Scotland:
http://fms.scot

Under-water video of Atlantic salmon spawning:
www.youtube.com/watch?v=uZDA51tFdug

Video of a bear catching Pacific salmon in Alaska:
www.youtube.com/watch?v=EurWaA7qCDw

Conclusions

A female Scottish crossbill, feeding on rowan berries   © Laurie Campbell

WHAT CAN WE CONCLUDE, FROM THE EVIDENCE PRESENTED IN THIS BOOK? HAS DNA TECHNOLOGY ALREADY REACHED ITS PEAK, OR WILL IT BECOME MORE USEFUL IN THE FUTURE? ARE CHILDREN IN SCOTLAND INTERESTED IN WILDLIFE CONSERVATION? OR ARE THEY ONLY INTERESTED IN MOBILE PHONES AND COMPUTER GAMES?

DNA and the future

Last week, a news article was published about a hand-held machine that can rapidly sequence an entire human genome. The same machine can be used to check for the presence of dangerous pathogens, such as the Ebola virus, in just a few minutes. When I started my PhD ten years ago, it took me an entire day to do DNA tests (for the DNA of a pathogen which can kill amphibians). Some local councils are considering the use of DNA tests to identify dogs with irresponsible owners. People who

IN 2018, THE IVORY TRADE WAS BANNED IN CHINA, WHICH SHOULD HELP TO
STOP THE KILLING OF WILD ELEPHANTS FOR THEIR IVORY. DNA TECHNOLOGY
CAN BE USED TO DETECT ILLEGAL PRODUCTS MADE FROM ENDANGERED
ANIMALS, SUCH AS ELEPHANT IVORY, RHINO HORN AND TIGER BONE.

fail to pick up after their dogs may be prosecuted, using DNA evidence. Some people argue that this is an example of 'surveillance' going too far but others think it is a good idea.

As you have seen in this book, DNA technology is widely used in wildlife conservation in Scotland. I have not managed to cover everything and I must apologise to some of the species which I have failed to mention, such as the Scottish crossbill and the Arran whitebeam tree, which have been identified as separate species with the help of DNA technology. In this book, I have described examples from Scotland because this project was funded by the Heritage Lottery Fund for Scotland but DNA-based research is helping to save wildlife across the world.

In 2018, the ivory trade was banned in China, which should help to stop the killing of wild elephants for their ivory. DNA technology can be used to detect illegal products made from endangered animals, such as elephant ivory, rhino horn and tiger bone. But it can be used in many other ways, for instance to identify illegal timber from endangered trees. Tropical hardwood trees are often illegally cut down and deliberately mis-labelled, so they can be sold for a huge profit in other countries.

DNA technology has its limitations. It does not always work perfectly. When testing ponds for the presence of great

crested newt DNA in Scotland, as part of this project, we found that the DNA test did not always detect the newts. On a few occasions, we could see great crested newts in the water when we were doing the sampling but the DNA test was negative. In these cases, there might not have been enough DNA in the water for our test to detect it. However, we did find some 'new' great crested newt sites and volunteers enjoyed testing the DNA-based method.

Sometimes, improvements in DNA testing lead to different conclusions. For years, scientists have been trying to work out whether modern humans interbred, or hybridised, with the Neanderthals. The Neanderthals were a closely-related species, or sub-species of 'hominid' in the same animal family as modern humans. They probably lived in Europe and Asia until about 40,000 years ago.

In 2004, the results of an analysis of mitochondrial DNA (mtDNA) from modern humans and Neanderthals suggested that there was little, if any, hybridisation between us and the Neanderthals. As mentioned earlier in this book, mtDNA is nearly all inherited from the mother, so it appears that female Neanderthals did not contribute greatly to the modern human population (based on analysis of mtDNA extracted from a small number of Neanderthal bones).

Adder by Mackenzie Robison, Park Primary School   Wildcat by Merryn Lloyd-Jones, Coldingham Primary School

In 2010 a different study, which included analysis of nuclear DNA, suggested that there was some interbreeding, with modern humans having up to 4% Neanderthal DNA. So, the Neanderthals might not be completely extinct, after all. In ten years time, the conclusions may have changed again, if more Neanderthal bones are found, or if the DNA technology improves.

DNA technology is just one of many brilliant, recent inventions that wildlife conservationists now use on a regular basis. Motion-sensitive cameras help us to detect animals that are very secretive, or are only active after dark. Pattern-recognition software programs can be used to recognise individual animals from digital photographs. Man-made satellites, orbiting far above the Earth, send back images which show us where wildlife habitat is being damaged.

With all of these technologies, it is possible to collect a vast amount of information in a short period of time. So we have to think very carefully about what we are going to do, in order to get the best possible value from the limited amount of funding that is available for wildlife conservation.

Wildlife art and writing

From the competition entries, we can conclude that there are children in Scotland who are deeply concerned about the welfare of wild animals. When we promoted the competition, we provided the children with a list of animals but we did not make any suggestions about what they should write.

Several of the writing entries focused upon the effects of hunting on animals, the hazards that animals face when crossing roads and the effects of habitat destruction. In *Saving the boys and the forest* Skye Dalli (from Park Primary School in Stranraer) wrote: "At dawn, the Scottish wild animals woke up to the sound of chainsaws. They were hacking down the animal's forest."

Skye Dalli's piece reminded me of *The Animals of Farthing Wood* by Colin Dann, a book which probably does not appeal to many adult scientists but helped to encourage my early interest in wildlife.

We need more people to develop a life-long interest in wildlife conservation. Many children of primary school age are delighted to talk about wildlife but for some reason, a love of nature is sometimes regarded as childish by

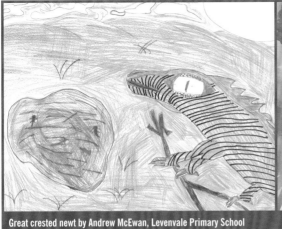

Great crested newt by Andrew McEwan, Levenvale Primary School

Red deer by Kathryn Hamilton, Drummore Primary School

older children and adults. During my visits to schools around Scotland during this project, I was besieged by young children who could not wait to tell me their stories about their encounters with wild animals. It is certainly not the case that children are only interested in mobile phones and computers. But if you present them with a jar full of newts, there is a good chance that they will use their phones to photograph it (why not?).

Some of the art entries reduced me to tears (in a good way!). The portrait of a golden eagle by Amy O'Keefe (which arrived in the ordinary post) left me unable to think about anything else for the rest of the day. This drawing is surely just as good as any professional art on sale in a commercial gallery. I hope that the young artists and writers featured in this book will go on to produce many more masterpieces and be properly rewarded for their talent and hard work.

Many thanks to everyone who took part in this project and helped to make it a success.

Pete Minting
February 2018

DURING MY VISITS TO SCHOOLS AROUND SCOTLAND DURING THIS PROJECT, I WAS BESIEGED BY YOUNG CHILDREN WHO COULD NOT WAIT TO TELL ME THEIR STORIES ABOUT THEIR ENCOUNTERS WITH WILD ANIMALS. IT IS CERTAINLY NOT THE CASE THAT CHILDREN ARE ONLY INTERESTED IN MOBILE PHONES AND COMPUTERS.

Pine marten by Orlaith Heggie of Sgoil nan Loch

Competition winners

Category	Age group	Place	Name	School (or independent)	Area
Art	A (P4-P5)	1st	Lewis McCulloch	Inverarary Primary School	Argyll
Art	A (P4-P5)	2nd	Andrew McEwan	Levenvale Primary School	Alexandria
Art	A (P4-P5)	3rd	Kathryn Hamilton	Drummore Primary School	Stranraer
Art	A (P4-P5)	HC	Owen McKelvey	Leadhills Primary School	S Lanarks
Art	A (P4-P5)	HC	Mackenzie Robison	Park Primary School	Stranraer
Art	B (P6-P7)	1st	Christina Matheson	Sgoil nan Loch	Lewis
Art	B (P6-P7)	2nd	Rose Wheal	Melrose Primary School	Borders
Art	B (P6-P7)	3rd	Merryn Lloyd-Jones	Coldingham Primary School	Borders
Art	B (P6-P7)	HC	Orlaith Heggie	Sgoil nan Loch	Lewis
Art	B (P6-P7)	HC	Marshall Markham	Drummore Primary School	Stranraer
Art	C (S1-S3)	1st	Amy O'Keefe	Greenfaulds High School	N Lanarks
Art	C (S1-S3)	2nd	Jenny O'Gorman	George Watson's College	Edinburgh
Art	C (S1-S3)	3rd	Kyle Diack	Greenfaulds High School	N Lanarks
Art	C (S1-S3)	HC	Mia Beattie	Lockerbie Academy	Dumfries
Art	C (S1-S3)	HC	Amelie Berry	Earlston High School	Borders
Art	C (S1-S3)	HC	Deena Lowery	Lockerbie Academy	Dumfries
Art	C (S1-S3)	HC	Anthony Ison	Lockerbie Academy	Dumfries
Art	C (S1-S3)	HC	Stuart Henderson	Belmont House School	Renfrewshire
Art	D (S4-S6)	1st	Rachel Simpson	Arbroath Academy	Angus
Art	D (S4-S6)	2nd	Cameron Glen	Arbroath Academy	Angus

Category	Age group	Place	Name	School (or independent)	Area
Art	D (S4-S6)	3rd	Navya Saini	Williamwood High School	Renfrewshire
Art	D (S4-S6)	HC	Saul McGivney	Arbroath Academy	Angus
Art	D (S4-S6)	HC	Seanna McNeill	Arbroath Academy	Angus
Writing	A (P4-P5)	1st	Euan Dillon	Troqueer Primary	Dumfries
Writing	A (P4-P5)	2nd	Jack Findlay	Troqueer Primary	Dumfries
Writing	A (P4-P5)	3rd	Iona Dillon	Troqueer Primary	Dumfries
Writing	A (P4-P5)	HC	Skye Dalli	Park Primary	Stranraer
Writing	A (P4-P5)	HC	Clara Lawrence	Leadhills Primary	S Lanarks
Writing	B (P6-P7)	1st	Luke Thomson	Melrose Primary	Borders
Writing	B (P6-P7)	2nd	Mila Todd	Monymusk Primary	Aberdeen
Writing	B (P6-P7)	3rd	Aiden Phommavanh	Monymusk Primary	Aberdeen
Writing	B (P6-P7)	HC	Ella Moroney-Lavin	(independent)	Edinburgh
Writing	B (P6-P7)	HC	Poppy Young	Coldingham Primary	Borders
Writing	C (S1-S3)	1st	Cheryl McIntyre	Ardnamurchan High	Lochaber
Writing	C (S1-S3)	2nd	Christopher Queen	St Joseph's Academy	E Ayrshire
Writing	C (S1-S3)	3rd	Leah Stanley	St Joseph's Academy	E Ayrshire
Writing	C (S1-S3)	HC	Cona Maitland	St Joseph's Academy	E Ayrshire
Writing	C (S1-S3)	HC	Craig McCowan	Ardnamurchan High	Lochaber
Writing	C (S1-S3)	HC	Archie Campbell	Ardnamurchan High	Lochaber
Writing	D (S4-S6)	1st	Gurpreet Kaur	(independent)	Glasgow

Acknowledgements

The award winners, Pete Minting (ARC) and wildlife artist Cherith Harrison at Edinburgh Zoo in October 2017

Artwork and writing by children from across Scotland

Many children from across Scotland helped to create this book, by providing artwork and writing for the chapters about Scottish animals which are being helped by DNA technology. We ran a competition during 2016 and 2017 to encourage participation and provide a way of selecting entries for inclusion in the book. A table listing the award winners is included on the following page.

We have included all of the winning entries in the book, plus many others which were of high quality. For some of the writing entries, it was not possible to include the entire entry but we have included some sections or quotes which are relevant to the main text of the book.

We would like to thank all of the children who submitted entries for the competition and the many teachers and parents who provided support and encouragement.

Event support

We would also like to thank the competition judges (led by Catriona Malan from Helensburgh Writers Workshop), the Royal Zoological Society of Scotland (RZSS) for providing a venue for the awards day and the following organisations who helped to fund, or donate prizes:

The Heritage Lottery Fund (Scotland), Scottish Natural Heritage (SNH), the Field Studies Council (FSC), Amphibian and Reptile Conservation (ARC), Caledonian Conservation Ltd, Cherith Harrison Ltd, The Mount Whistle Company and the Hugh Fraser Foundation.

Many thanks to staff from RZSS, especially Gill Murray-Dickson, who helped to organise the awards day for the competition which was held at Edinburgh Zoo on 21 October 2017, followed by a one-day conference for adults, entitled *DNA technology and the conservation of Scottish wildlife*, on 22 October 2017.

Book production

Thanks also to the following people and organisations who made a major contribution towards the production of this book, in terms of providing photographs, or reviewing the content and design:

Gill Murray-Dickson, Helen Senn, Ben Harrower, Dave Barclay and Sian Addison (RZSS), Roo Campbell (SNH), Duncan McKenzie (Scottish Wildcat Action), Lizzie Croose and Robert Cruickshanks (Vincent Wildlife Trust), Sarah Hoy and Mick Marquiss (University of Aberdeen), Phil Whitfield (Natural Research Ltd), Laura White (Sustrans), Jenny Shelton and Ian Thomson (RSPB), Paul Kirkland (Butterfly Conservation), Josephine Pemberton (University of Edinburgh), Fred Holmes, Chris Dresh, John Wilkinson, Angela Reynolds, Angie Julian and Liam Russell (ARC), Erik Paterson (Clyde Amphibian and Reptile Group), Caroline Walker, Rodger McPhail, Sherryn Ciavaglia (SASA), Sylvain Ursenbacher (University of Basel), Richard Sutcliffe (Glasgow Museum), Laurie Campbell (Laurie Campbell Photography), Jason Holderness (The Design Unit Ltd), Rosie Lawson and Alison Hillis.